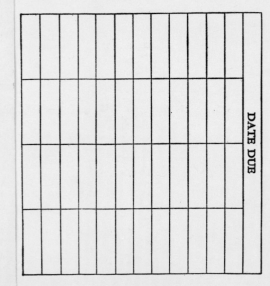

DATE DUE

NEW

FRENCH

WRITING

Edited by GEORGES BORCHARDT

CRITERION BOOKS
NEW YORK

840.8
B64n

Editor's Note

New French Writing will answer the curiosity of those who have discovered, after World War II, and more particularly in the past two or three years, a new, lively, often pungent French literature. The texts gathered here are not a digested version of the best France has produced over a certain period of time; they are samples of the most significant writing done in France today, by some of France's most significant writers; they are works, or excerpts from works, some of which have not yet been printed even in France (none, with the exception of the selection from *In the Labyrinth,* has been translated into English heretofore). In other words, *New French Writing* is designed to give its readers an idea of the "situation" of French literature today, and a foretaste of things to come.

The selections, of course, speak for themselves. Just a few words, then, about their authors.

Jean-Paul Sartre, perhaps more than his contemporaries, has been consistently concerned with the role of the artist in society. This may be why three of his current works in progress are devoted either to a writer (himself, and Flaubert) or to a painter (Tintoretto). This may also be why, although his literary influence seems small today, his works are always impatiently awaited by a large following (his latest play, *Les Sequestrés d'Altona,* is a hit of the current season in Paris).

The two playwrights represented here stand at opposite poles of the world of the stage. Félicien Marceau, a successful novelist (*The China Shepherdess, Heartflights*) turned to the theater a few years ago and produced two hits, *The Egg* and *The Good Soup.* He probably is, with Jean Anouilh, the most popular playwright in France today. The least popular, on the other hand, may well be Jean Vauthier, whose plays have won the recognition of such actor-producers as Jean Vilar and Jean-Louis Barrault, but whose following is as yet much smaller than Samuel Beckett's, Jean Genet's or Arthur Adamov's.

Pierre Gascar won the Prix Goncourt for his *Beasts and Men.* In addition to this volume of short stories, he has also written several novels (among these, *The Seed*), and is generally considered one of the best writers of his generation (and its best short-story writer).

Alain Robbe-Grillet is the theoretician of the "new novel," about which he has written in *Evergreen Review.* His "anti-psychological" novels include *The Voyeur* and *Jealousy,* and the text presented here is part of his fourth and latest one. He is usually mentioned in one breath with Michel Butor, a winner of the Prix Renaudot, who in France has reached a much wider audience. Butor, the author of *A Change of Heart,* has just completed his fourth novel, and the excerpt from it that is presented here indicates that the author is still fascinated by the changes (not of heart alone) brought about by time.

Pierre Klossowski, author of a book on Sade and of a translation of Kafka's journal, has with three short novels created his own *"univers romanesque,"* at once metaphysical and highly erotic. With his latest book he has graduated from the "limited-edition" category to reach a wider and growing reading public.

Germaine Brée and Henri Peyre are French but living in the

United States. Through their books and essays they have for many years presented contemporary French works to English-speaking readers.

Marc Alyn, Yves Bonnefoy, and Philippe Jaccottet are three of the poets introduced in Germaine Brée's essay.

As for the translators, Richard Howard has to his credit two novels by Robbe-Grillet, one by Pieyre de Mandiargues, two by Claude Simon, and many other books; he is now writing a novel of his own. D'Elbert Keenan is a professor of French at New York University. Ursule Molinaro and Venable Herndon are co-editors of the *Chelsea Review;* she adapted a play by François Mauriac and has written plays and short stories of her own; he is a poet. Anne Borchardt translated a play by Marguerite Duras, as well as short pieces by Mauriac, Félicien Marceau and others.

Contents

7

FROM A STUDY ON Tintoretto

by JEAN-PAUL SARTRE

translated by RICHARD HOWARD

1. *Les Fourberies de Jacopo*

Nothing. This life has been swallowed up. Some dates, a few
facts, and then the chatter of dead authors. But we need not be
discouraged—*Venice will speak to us,* and her voice, sometimes
shrill, sometimes whispering, broken by silences bearing false
witness, is his own. Tintoretto's biography, a portrait of the
artist painted in his lifetime by his birthplace, betrays a tireless
animosity. The City of the Doges informs us she has taken a
dislike to her most famous son. Nothing is spoken: a glance,
a suggestion, then we move on. Such inflexible hatred is as inconsistent as sand; more than outright aversion, it has all the
chill, the surliness, the insidious vagueness of rejection. We ask
for nothing more: Jacopo joins an equivocal combat with his
limitless adversary, exhausts himself, and dies defeated; that,
essentially, is his life. We shall see it in all its lurid nakedness
if we clear away the underbrush of gossip that clutters the
approach.

Jacopo is born in 1518; his father is a dyer; and straightway
Venice whispers in our ear that the whole thing has begun very
badly: *around 1530, the boy enters Titian's workshop as an*

apprentice, but after a few days the fifty-year-old master discovers he is a genius and shows him the door. As plain as that. We have this anecdote from many pens, with an insistence that ends by catching our attention. It is scarcely flattering to Titian, you will say. And, as a matter of fact, it is not; or at least, not *today*, not in our eyes. But by the time Vasari tells the story, in 1567, Titian has been the reigning master for half a century: nothing is more worthy of respect than a long impunity. Then too, according to the rules of the period, he is, after God, Master in his own studio: we will not refuse him the right to sack an employee. Victims, on the contrary, are presumed guilty: stigmatized by misfortune, contagious perhaps, they have the evil eye. In short, this is the first time that an accursed childhood figures in the *legenda aurea* of the Italian painters. Doubtless there's something to be gleaned here: but later. The Voice of Venice never lies, on condition that we know how to listen to it; we shall attend to what it says when we are better informed. For the moment, whatever the real truth of the matter, we must underline the improbability of the facts.

Titian, we know, was not an easy man. But Jacopo was twelve years old. At twelve, the *gift* is nothing, a trifle can smother it: patience and time must "set" a fragile facility in order to transform it into talent; at the peak of his fame even the touchiest artist is hardly likely to take umbrage at a mere boy. But let us suppose, for argument's sake, that the jealous Master has repudiated his apprentice; which comes down to assassinating him. The malediction of an official genius, a national glory, weighs heavily, very heavily. Particularly since Titian has not been so ingenuous as to reveal his real motives; once the king frowns, all doors are closed to the black sheep; his very profession is forbidden him.

It is not every day that we see a child blacklisted. Our interest stirs, we wonder how he got out of such a fix. It is no use: at this moment the thread of the narrative breaks, in every source,

every reference; we are up against a conspiracy of silence—
between twelve and twenty, no one will tell us what has become
of him. One way of filling this gap is to suppose he educated
himself. But that is the one thing we know to be impossible,
and the dead authors know it still better: at the beginning of
the sixteenth century, the art of painting is still a complicated,
rather ceremonious technique, encumbered by a tangle of
rituals and recipes, a knack more than a knowledge, a com-
pendium of procedures rather than a method; professional
canons, studio traditions, everything tends to make apprenticeship a necessary social obligation. The biographers' silence betrays their embarrassment; unable to reconcile young Robusti's
precocious notoriety with his excommunication, they draw a
veil of vagueness over the eight years separating the one from
the other. Which we may consider as an admission: no one has
repudiated Jacopo; if he hasn't pined away from sloth and spite
in his father's dye works, he must have worked regularly,
normally, in the workshop of some painter we know nothing
about save that *it was not Titian.* In guarded, suspicious soci-
eties, hatred is retrospective; if the mysterious beginning of this
life seems a premonition of its mysterious close, if the curtain
raised on a miraculously averted disaster falls on a disaster
without divine intervention, it is because Venice has rearranged
the evidence after the fact to stigmatize a child by his future
old age. Nothing happens and nothing lasts, birth is the mirror
of death; between the two lies so much scorched earth; everything is tainted by bad luck.

If we ford these mirages, the view is clearer on the other
side, we can see all the way to the horizon: a youth appears
who starts in high gear and speeds toward glory. In 1539,
Jacopo leaves his master to set up as a painter on his own; he
is a *past master.* This young businessman has conquered independence, fame, a clientele, and hires artisans, apprentices, in
his turn. Let there be no mistake: in a city glutted with painters,

where economic crisis threatens to paralyze the market, being a master at twenty is an exception; such an achievement cannot be attributed to merit alone, nor to industry, nor to tact; it requires good luck. Consider Robusti's fortune: Veronese is ten, Titian sixty-two; between this unknown child and this old man who will certainly not last much longer, we can find any number of good painters, but only Tintoretto promises to be great; in his generation, at any rate, he has no rival: the way is clear. And, as a matter of fact, he continues on his own momentum for several years more: commissions multiply, he enjoys public favor as well as the esteem of aristocrats and connoisseurs; Aretino himself deigns to congratulate him; this young painter enjoys the supernatural facility Providence reserves for those who are to die young. But he doesn't die, and the trouble begins: Titian gives every evidence of an astounding longevity and lavishes all the attentions of hatred on his young challenger; the old monarch is sly enough to designate his official successor, and, as we suspected, it is Veronese; Aretino's condescension turns to bitterness; the critics pinch, bite, scratch, and shriek; they are modernizing themselves. Yet this would be unimportant if Jacopo retained the good graces of the public. But suddenly the wheel turns. At thirty, sure of his powers, he asserts his mastery in *Saint Mark Rescuing the Slave* and puts everything he has into it. To take by surprise, to strike hard and seize unawares is indeed his way. Yet for once he is the first to be disconcerted: the work not only stuns but scandalizes his contemporaries, among whom he finds relentless detractors but no stubborn defenders; in the background is the hint of a cabal: a stop thrust.[1] Face to face, united and separated by the same uneasiness, Venice and her painter stare at each other and no longer understand what they see. "Jacopo," the city says, "has not lived up to the promise of his

---

1. Ridolfi even claims that the Scuola San Marco refused the canvas and that Tintoretto was obliged to take it back.

adolescence." And the artist: "To disappoint them, all I had
to do was show myself. It certainly wasn't *me* they used to like!"
This misunderstanding degenerates into malice on both sides:
a thread has snapped in the Venetian web.

The crucial year is 1548: *before,* the gods are with him;
after, against. Not great disasters, only bad luck: but sicken-
ingly; as if they had granted the child their smiles only to destroy
the man more readily. Suddenly Jacopo is transformed into
himself, becomes that frenzied and fugitive outlaw, Tintoretto.
Before, we know nothing about him save that he worked like a
devil; you cannot make a name for yourself at twenty without
a passion for work. *After,* this passion turns to rage: he must
produce, endlessly produce, sell, crush his rivals by the number
and the size of his canvases. There is something desperate in
this forcing: until his death, Robusti works against the clock,
and we cannot determine if he is trying to find himself in his
work or escape himself in overwork. Captain Tintoretto sails
under a black flag; for this swift pirate, all means are justified.
Generous when generosity pays, he lowers his eyes, refuses to
name his price, and childishly repeats: "It will be just what
you want." But the porters of Naples know best how profitable
carrying baggage is: they let their customer fleece himself, out
of generosity.

On other occasions, to seal a bargain, he offers his wares at
cost: this ruinous contract will bring in others, and these more
advantageous. He learns that the *Crociferi* are about to give a
commission to Paolo Cagliari, pretends to know nothing about
it and offers his services. Politely, they try to get rid of him:
"With pleasure, but we want a Veronese." "A Veronese—fine,"
he says. "And who's to paint you one?" "Who?" comes the
astonished answer, "who else could we have been thinking of
but Paolo Cagliari. . . ." And Tintoretto, astonished in his
turn: "Cagliari? What a strange notion. I'll paint you a better
Veronese than he can. And for less." Contract signed, and

promise kept. This sort of thing repeated twenty times over—
Tintoretto does a Pordenone, a Titian, always at a discount.

How to cut his costs? The question plagues him. One day
he hits on the answer, an inspired and niggardly one that will
upset a whole tradition: habitually the masters have their
canvases copied; their studios execute replicas and sell them at
greatly reduced prices: in other words, painters have a kind
of "reproductions" market. To attract customers, Jacopo offers
better for *less*: he withdraws the models; his canvases may
provide inspiration but may not be *imitated;* by simple, in-
variable procedures, his collaborators will make new works
without having to invent: all they need to do is reverse the composition, put the left on the right, the right on the left, take an
old man from some other picture and substitute him for a
woman who, thereby liberated, can serve again somewhere else.
These operations require a certain amount of practice, but take
no more time than the mere labor of reproduction; Tintoretto
frankly proclaims: "In my studio you can acquire an original
for the price of a copy."

When no one wants his canvases, he gives them away. On
May 31, 1564, in the Scuola San Rocco, the leaders of the Guild
decide to decorate the hall where their meetings are held: the
central oval of the ceiling is to be embellished with a painted
canvas. Paolo Cagliari, Jacopo Robusti, Schiavone, Salviati
and Zucearo are invited to submit sketches. Tintoretto bribes
the servants, obtains the exact dimensions of the areas to be
painted. He has already worked for the Guild, and I am not
overlooking the hypothesis that he found accomplices within
the *"Banca e Zonta"* itself. On the appointed day, each artist
offers his sketches; when it is Robusti's turn, thunder and
lightning! He climbs up a ladder, pulls away a curtain, and
reveals overhead his dazzling painting, already complete, already in place. Murmurs. He explains: "A sketch can be mis-
interpreted; while I was at it, I preferred to complete my work.

But if this painting does not please you, Gentlemen, I offer it as a gift—not to you, but to your patron Saint Rocco, who has shown me such kindness." This is forcing their hand, and the astute painter knows it: the Guild statutes forbid the refusal of any pious donations. There is nothing left to do but record the event in the Scuola's books: "Upon this day, the under-signed Jacopo Tintoretto, painter, has offered us a painting; he asks for no remuneration, promises to do any further work required upon it and declares himself satisfied." And the under-signed writes in his turn: "*Io Jachomo Tentoretto pitor contento et prometo ut supra.*"

Contento? I should think so! This offering sows panic among his rivals, opens all the doors of the Scuola to him, yields immense and naked walls to the fury of his brushes and ends by bringing him an annual pension of a hundred ducats. He is, indeed, so content that he pulls the same trick in 1571. This time in the Doges' Palace. The Signoria wishes to commemorate the Battle of Lepanto; it organizes a competition of designs. Tintoretto brings a painting and bestows it. It is accepted with gratitude; a short time afterwards, he sends his bill.

In this infamous and engaging confidence game we may see, perhaps, a trait more characteristic of the manners of the period than of Jacopo's character. The crook, you will say, is not Tintoretto but his age; and you are partly right. If someone wanted to condemn him on the basis of such anecdotes, I know everything the defense would say. This first of all, which is the most serious argument: at the time, no one could *work for himself*. Today, art is a picture sale; in that age, it was a sale of painters. They stood in the square like *bracchiante* in the southern towns; the prospective buyers arrived, examined them all, and chose one whom they carried off to their church, their *scuola*, their *palazzo*. The painter had to offer himself, show himself like our stage directors, accept any commission just as the latter, in the wild hope of showing their skill, accept any script. Everything was arranged by contract: the subject, the number, rank, and sometimes even the attitude of the characters, the size of the canvas; religious tradition and period taste added their tabus. The customers had the moods, the whims of our theatrical producers. They had, alas, their sudden inspirations as well; at a sign from them, everything was done over. In the Medici Palace, Benozzo Gozzoli was endlessly and ingeniously tortured by one stupid Mycenas after another; in Tintoretto's case we need only compare the Louvre *Paradise* with the one in the Doges' Palace to divine the nature of the pressures he has endured. Intransigence, the refusal to compromise, the proud choice of poverty are impossible attitudes: the family must be fed and the studio kept working, like today's machines. In short, you must give up painting or paint to order. No one can reproach Tintoretto for merely wanting to get rich; certainly toward the middle of his life he was never without work and there was no lack of money coming in; the principle of this utilitarian was that one should do nothing for nothing: painting would be merely a pastime if it did not *earn*. Later on he buys himself a rather plebian house in a working-class neighborhood of Venice; his new-found security is the crown of his career. But all his savings have gone into this purchase and the Robusti children will share a pathetic legacy: the studio equipment, a shrinking clientele, and then the house itself, which goes to the elder son, then to the son-in-law. Twelve years after her husband's death, Faustina bitterly remembers how he left his family in straitened circumstances; she is right to complain: the deceased thought only of himself. He enjoyed money, no doubt about that, but in the American way: regarding it as merely the outward emblem of his success. Actually, this contract chaser asks only one thing: the means to practice his trade. And then, his frauds are somewhat justified: they would not even be conceivable if he did not at least redeem them by professional skill, a passion for work, and amazing promptitude:

it is his *sprint* that gives Jacopo his advantage: to paint a good picture he needs no more time than others take over bad sketches.

Moreover, if he plagiarized Veronese, the latter returned the compliment often enough. We must look at these reciprocal borrowings through the eyes of their contemporaries. For many of these, the greatest painters are merely trade names, juridical and collective personalities. In our case, it is *this* picture we want first and foremost. Afterwards, through it, it is the whole man: we hang Matisse on our walls. But take the case of the *Crociferi:* they were quite unconcerned with Cagliari; they wanted a certain style that suited them perfectly, an inspired stupidity, a trim and untroubled splendor; they knew a trade mark, a slogan: a painting signed Veronese is a painting that makes you comfortable. That was what they wanted, and that was all. Cagliari himself could do better, as he has proved by painting his *Calvary*,[2] but he was too good a businessman to overtax his genius. Under such conditions, it would be unfair to blame Tintoretto for occasionally appropriating a manner that actually belonged to no one man. After all, he made an honest enough proposition: "Is mindless vivacity what you want? I'll give it to you."

I concede the truth of all these reproaches, for we are not concerned with judging him: what we want to know is if his age recognized itself in him without difficulty or discomfort. And on this point the testimony is unquestionable: his methods shocked his contemporaries, and he was called to account for them. A degree of perfidy might have been countenanced, but Tintoretto went too far; all Venice echoed to a single cry: "He exaggerates!" Even in a mercantile city, this overly cunning merchant cornered the market. In the Scuola San Rocco, his confrères complained so bitterly when he pirated their com-

2. In the Louvre. Paradoxically, he has taken his inspiration from the *genuine* Robusti.

mission that he felt obliged to appease them: the building had other ceilings, other walls, the work was only beginning; as for himself, once his offering was accepted he would withdraw, leaving the field open to those more worthy. It did not take long to discover he was lying like any Turk: the Scuola was to become his fief; in his lifetime, not a single other painter would cross the threshold. Not that anyone had waited for this occasion to hate him. It will be noticed, however, that the scandal occurred in 1561 and that the first "Life" of Tintoretto appeared in 1567: this comparison of dates might enlighten us as to the origin and significance of the spiteful gossip Vasari has collected. Jealous slanders? But everyone was slandered by jealousy, when the occasion called for it; why should calumny dog Robusti alone, unless he is in the artists' "bad odor," unless he represents in every man's eyes the failings of his neighbor concentrated in a single man and carried to the extreme degree? The customers themselves, moreover, seem shocked by his procedures. Not all of them, of course; but he had made many and determined enemies. Messire Zammaria di Zigninoni, a member of the Guild of San Rocco, offers fifteen ducats toward the costs of decoration, on the express condition that Jacopo is not to undertake it. The Guild's records, furthermore, indicate that the *"Banca e Zonta,"* after its hand was forced, held several delicate and somewhat disturbed sessions in the Scuola itself, beneath the coruscation of this cumbrous donation; an agreement was reached, but Messire di Zigninoni kept his ducats. Nor did the city officials always seem well disposed. In 1571 Tintoretto bestows his *Battle of Lepanto;* in 1577 the painting is destroyed by a fire; when the question of replacing it arises, its creator seems justified in supposing that the Signoria will call upon him. This is not the case, however: Tintoretto is deliberately passed over in favor of the mediocre Vicentino. It may be objected that the first picture had not been approved of. But this is hardly likely: Jacopo takes every precaution when he works for officials; he "paints a Titian," he stays in hiding. Moreover, since 1571 the government has commissioned him to execute other works. No: the government of Venice has no intention of denying itself his services; it desires to punish him for his piratical practices. In short, everyone agrees he is a treacherous confrère, an unlicensed interloper, and there must be something rotten about him if we do not know the name of a single one of his friends. Suppose that, though you are disquieted by the evidence, you are high-minded and therefore accustomed to employ the dead for the edification of the living; you may interpret Jacopo's excesses as infallible proofs of his passion. Yet passions have as many aspects as people: devouring, meditative, visionary, carping, practical, abstract, loitering, precipitous—and a hundred others. Tintoretto's I should call practical, anxious-recriminatory, and devouring-precipitous. The more I think about his absurd intrigues, the more I am convinced that they originated in an agonized heart. What a viper's tangle! Everything is there: the obsessions of pride and the abyss of humility, narrow ambitions and limitless confusion, fury and misfortune, the will to succeed and the will to fail. His life is the campaign of a panic-stricken *arriviste;* it begins briskly enough with a well-planned offensive and then, after the setback of 1548, its rhythm accelerates and goes haywire, it becomes an inferno; Jacopo will beat his own record until he dies, but he knows he will never win. *Arrivisme* and anxiety: these are the largest vipers. If we really want to know him, let us step closer and examine them.

2. *The Puritans of the Rialto*

No one is a cynic. Mortification for its own sake is the amusement of the saints. Only to a certain point: these prudes stigmatize their own lubricity, these philanthropists chasten their own avarice. But should they discover their real gangrene, sanctity, they run after justifications like any sinner. Tintoretto is not a saint; he knows that the whole city condemns his behavior; if he persists, it is because he believes he is in the right against Venice. Nor are we convinced by being told that he is aware of his own genius: genius is a stupid wager that knows what it dares, not what it is worth. Nothing is more miserable than such fretful temerity that cries for the moon and dies without obtaining it: pride comes first, with neither proofs nor passport; at its extreme, we may call it genius, but I fail to see what we have gained. No: Tintoretto justifies his piracies by neither the simple plenitude of his skill nor the infinite abyss of his aspirations: he is defending his rights; each time one of his confrères receives a commission, Jacopo is being wronged. Left to himself he will cover all the city's walls with his paintings, no *campo* will be too large, no *sotto portico* too dark for him to illuminate; he will daub the floors, the citizens will walk over his finest images, his brush will spare neither the façades on the Grand Canal nor the gondolas nor perhaps the gondoliers. This man imagines he has received, by being born in it, the privilege of transforming his city into himself, and in a way we can maintain that he is right.

When he begins his apprenticeship, painting is in a quandary. In Florence, there is an outright crisis; Venice, as usual, holds its tongue or lies; but we have formal proof that the genuinely Rialtine sources of inspiration are drained. At the end of the fifteenth century, the city is profoundly influenced by the visit of Antonello da Messina. This is a decisive event: henceforth, Venice imports her painters. Not that she goes far to look for them: the fact remains, however, that the most famous come from *terra firma*—Giorgione, from Castelfranco; Titian, from Preve di Cadere, Paolo Cagliari and Bonifazio dei Pitati, from Verona; Palma the Elder, from Bergamo; Girolamo the Elder and Pariso Bordone, from Treviso; Andrea Schiavone, from Zara; and so on. In fact, this aristocratic republic is primarily a technocracy, it has always been bold enough to recruit its specialists from all over the world, and astute enough to treat them as its own children. Besides, this is the period when the Most Serene Republic, checkmated at sea, threatened by coalitions on the continent, turns toward the country behind it and tries to assert its power by conquests: the new immigrants are, for the most part, natives of annexed territories. Yet by this massive importation of talent Venice betrays her anxiety; when we remember that most of the *quattrocento* artists were born within the walls or on Murano, we must realize that a continuity of generations would have been impossible—after the extinction of the Vivarini and Bellini families, after the death of Carpaccio—without a blood transfusion.

In painting as in other trades, it is the patrician class that facilitates the immigration of good artisans; it is this class that —evincing what we might call a cosmopolitan chauvinism— treats the Republic of the Doges as a kind of melting pot; in the eyes of this suspicious and jealous aristocracy, the best Venetians are foreigners: if they adopt Venice, it is because they have fallen in love with her; if they want to be accepted, they will be easily manipulated. But we can be sure that the native artisans do not regard the newcomers with the same favor; why should they? This is foreign competition. No one is so imprudent as to protest, a smiling welcome is the rule, but not without a struggle, not without constant tension, not without recriminatory pride. Obliged to yield to the technical superiority of these foreigners, the native workman conceals his humiliation by falling back on his prerogatives; he agrees to give ground to the more expert, the more skillful, but this is a sacrifice he makes to his country: his franchise remains intact. A Rialtino is *at home* in Venice; the German workers may know more about glass-blowing, but they will never have the *native grace*. Before they died out, the great *quattrocento* painters had the bitter fate of seeing the public turn away from them and accord its favors to young interlopers who scorned them. For instance Titian, himself an alien, left Gentile Bellini for his brother, Giovanni, only because he was in pursuit of another foreigner, Antonello da Messina, that meteor who had streaked across the sky and the waters of the lagoon twenty years before. Of Giovanni Bellini himself, Tiziano Vecellio has no need: it is a reflection, an echo that he seeks in him, as proved by the fact that he soon abandons the master for the disciple and takes lessons from Giorgione: this third outlander is regarded by the second as the true heir of the first. Yet Titian and Giorgione belong to the same generation; the pupil may even be older than the master. And on that day, the two Bellinis must have realized the end was at hand. And what about Giovanni's true disciples? What did they say? And what did the others think, the last representatives of the Muranese school? Many were still young men, or at least not old; they all felt Antonello's influence, but through the Bellinis; the color and the light originated in Messina, but Giovanni had acclimatized them; through him, they became Venetian. These men made it a point of honor to remain faithful, but their fidelity choked them; they tried to adapt themselves to the new demands without abandoning the somewhat primitive techniques they had been taught; this meant condemning themselves to mediocrity; how bitter it must have been for them to see the two young intruders join forces, break with the native traditions, rediscover the Sicilian's secrets and effortlessly carry painting to its highest perfection! Yet Giovanni still reigned, the fame of this admirable artist extended through all of northern Italy: the barbarian infiltration began during his last years; after his death—in 1516—came the deluge.

Yet at the height of the invasion the century's greatest painter was born in an alley of this occupied city. Melancholy plebeian pride, always abased, suppressed, forever on the alert, seized the occasion and slipped into the heart of the one Rialtino who still had talent, and then proceeded to inspire, to *ignite* him. We must remember that he did not come directly from the people, nor entirely from the bourgeoisie. His father was a well-paid artisan. Such *petits bourgeois* took pride from the fact that they did not work in other people's houses: as a laborer's son, Jacopo might have remained an obscure artist's assistant; as a master's son, he must become a master or lose caste; he will rise through the ranks, but the honor of his family and of his class forbid him to remain there. Naturally he was not gratefully remembered in the studio where he served his apprenticeship: he entered it only to leave as soon as possible and assume the place already reserved for him in the social hierarchy. And then what? Schiavone (or Pordenone or Bonifazio dei Pitati, they are all the same) doubtless considered him an intruder; but Jacopo, in return, regarded his master as a foreigner, in other words as a thief. This Little Dyer is a native, Venice is his by blood. Mediocre, he would have been content with modest resentment; but he is brilliant, he knows it, therefore he wishes to exceed all others. Foreigners, in the eyes of a Rialtino, have no protection other than their professional worth: if Jacopo surpasses them, they will have to disappear, even if he must assassinate them. No one paints or writes without sanction: would one dare if *Je* were not *un Autre?* Jacopo is authorized by an entire laboring population to reconquer by his art the privileges of the pure-blooded Venetian. This is what accounts for his good conscience: in him popular recrimination becomes an austere, revenging passion; he has been given the duty to compel recognition of his rights; to the man fighting for so just a cause no holds are barred to achieve its triumph: no forgiveness, no quarter. The unfortunate thing is that his struggle against the undesirables obliges him to oppose the patricians in the name of native artisanry, to refute their policy of assimilation. When he shouts through the streets: "Veronese in Verona!" it is the government he is casting a slur upon. No sooner does he realize this than he retreats a step, then immediately afterwards resumes his stubborn progress. Hence this curious mixture of severity and submission: the prudent subject of a police state, Jacopo always yields or pretends to yield; *autochthonous* citizen of the most beautiful city in the world, his arrogance explodes in spite of himself: for all his servility he never loses the ankylosis of his pride. To no avail: the intrigues he foments against the aristocracy's protégés he ruins by his own impatience, by irreparable blunders, or else they turn against him of their own accord. Which sheds a new light on the rancors of the Most Serene Republic. This citizen may be demanding no more than what will be granted him anyway, but such querulous submission irritates the Authorities: they regard him as a rebel. Or at the least as suspect, and indeed they are not mistaken. Consider, instead, where this first excess will lead him.

First of all, to that diligent and almost sadistic violence that I should call the total use of the self. Born among the common people who bear the weight of a heavily hierarchized society, Jacopo shares their fears and their preferences; we detect their prudence even in his presumption. His family, as cautious as they are courageous, have taught him the cost of things, the dangers of life, which hopes are permitted and which forbidden. Precise and prescribed opportunities, a legible destiny drawn up in advance, a half-open future, the all-too-distinct little bouquet imprisoned in the crystal paperweight—that is what destroys dreams: we covet only what we can. Such moderation drives the mad to violence, inspires the most frenzied ambitions, which are of short duration: Jacopo's ambition suddenly thrusts itself into being fully armed, with all its virulence and its variety, uniting with that tiny gleam of light, the possible. Or rather, nothing is *possible:* there is the end and the means, the specific task; you will rise above the heaviest clouds, the lowest ones, your hand will touch a taut, luminous skin which is the ceiling; there are other ceilings, other membranes, each lighter than the last, each thinner, and perhaps all the way at the top the blue of heaven itself. But Tintoretto has nothing to do with that; every man has his own powers of ascension, his own natural strength. Jacopo knows he is gifted, he has been told that talent is a kind of capital. If he gives evidence of his capacities, his enterprise will prosper and he will find means of fitting himself out. Now he is mobilized for the whole of a long life, his funds frozen: the vein is there to be worked until mine and miner are exhausted. During the same period, that other workhorse Michelangelo grows squeamish, starts work, disappears, leaves everything unfinished. Tintoretto *always* finishes, with the terrible application of the man who ends his sentences no matter what happens; even death waits on him in San Giorgio, lets him give his last brushstroke to his last picture, or at least his last directions to his assistants; his whole life long he has not permitted himself a whim, a distaste, a preference, not even the relaxation of a dream; he must have repeated this rule to himself, on days of fatigue: each time I refuse a commission I'm making a present to my confrères.

Produce at all costs! Here a man's will and that of a city meet. A hundred years before, Donatello reproached Uccello for sacrificing creation to research and for carrying his love of painting to the point of no longer producing pictures: but that was in Florence; the artists there had just ventured into the dangerous world of "perspective," attempting to construct a new plastic space by applying to the objects painted the laws of geometrical optics. *Autre temps, autres moeurs:* in Venice, under Titian's rule, everyone believed that painting had achieved its highest perfection, that there was nothing left to look for: art was dead, long live life. Barbarism begins with Aretino's inanities: "How alive it looks! How real! *You'd never think it was painted!*" In short, it is time for painting to yield to *realizations:* the inspired merchants want useful beauty. The work must give amateurs pleasure, advertise the republic's opulence throughout Europe, and strike the people with terror. The terror still endures: we gasp at the Venetian cinemascope; we, the tourist *canaille*, stunned by Titian's camera work, by a Paoli Cagliari production, by Pordenone's performance, by Vicentino's choreography. Jacopo Robusti shares the prejudices of his age, and our scholars still hold it against him. Now many times I've heard someone say: "Tintoretto, ugh —it's all movies!" Yet no one in the world, neither before him nor since, has carried the passion for experiment further. With Titian, painting chokes beneath its *beauties,* denies itself by its own perfections: in this death Jacopo sees the necessary condition of a resurrection: everything is beginning, everything is still to be done, as we shall see. But—and this is his great contradiction—Tintoretto will never permit his experiments to diminish his productivity. So long as even one bare wall remains in Venice, the painter's function is to cover it: morality forbids the transformation of a studio into a laboratory. Art is altogether a serious business and a struggle to the death against invaders. Like Titian, like Veronese, Jacopo will produce *cadavres exquis*. With one difference: these corpses are a prey to a fever of which we cannot say, at first, whether it is a renewal of life or the beginning of corruption. And if we would compare him to our movie makers at any price, it is *in this* that he resembles them: he accepts idiotic screenplays in order to load them in secret with his own obsessions. The customer must be fooled, must have his money's worth—he wants his Catherine, his Theresa or his Sebastian; for the same price he can appear on the canvas himself, with his wife or his brothers, if he insists. But clandestinely, behind the sumptuous and banal façade of this *realization,* Jacopo pursues his experiments; all his great works have a double significance: his narrow utilitarianism conceals an endless interrogation; confining his radicalism within the framework of the paid commission, he is obliged to revolutionize painting while respecting his client's stipulations.

This is the profound reason for his overwork, later on it will be the cause of his ruin.

Then too, the market must be cornered. We have seen how he has taken steps in this direction. But let us take another look at his methods; they look quite different from another angle. Tintoretto's revolt becomes a radical one: rebelling against the melting-pot policy, we find him obliged to infringe on corporative rulings or traditions. The government, unable to suppress the competition whose advantages it admits in other respects, now makes every effort to channel it by means of contests. Since it is their taste which will ultimately decide, the rich and the powerful will save law and order, will create this more flexible form of protectionism: controlled competition. Are they sincere? Certainly, and all would be well if we had evidence of their qualification. But we must take their word for this. It happens that they are fortunate in their gambling, and then, another time, they chose Vicentino. Tintoretto always manages to escape the test: does he deny them any capacity to judge? Of course not! He merely refuses them the right to treat a native Venetian on the same footing as the intruders. The fact remains that these contests exist: by avoiding them, our rebel deliberately undertakes to destroy protectionism. There is no way out: since the officials claim to judge by merit and since he rejects their judgment, he must give up painting or triumph by the quality of his work. Even so, he finds other means, outdistances his competitors, confronts the jurors with a *fait accompli,* puts his skill, his rapidity, the diligence of his assistants at the service of a mass production that explodes all reckonings by permitting him to sell his canvases at ruinous prices, occasionally even to give them away. On some Roman avenue, two secondhand shops stand opposite one another; the proprietors, I suppose, have agreed to simulate a merciless rivalry, unless both stalls have the same owner, a tragic comedian who enjoys confronting the two aspects of his nature in an eternal *vis-à-vis:*

on one storefront, black-bordered announcements: *"Prezzi disastrosi!"*, on the other, a show-window covered with vari-colored little signs: *"Prezzi da ridere! da ridere! da ridere!"* This has gone on for years, and I never see these two shops with-out their reminding me, both together, of Tintoretto. Had he chosen laughter or tears? Both, I think: it's up to the customer. We can even imagine that he sneered a little, in solitude, and that he complained *en famille,* shouting that his throat was being cut; nevertheless: in his studio, it was bargain day all year long, and the customer succumbed to the lure of these going-out-of-business prices. Originally intending to commis-sion a medallion, they ended by surrendering every wall in their house. It is Tintoretto who first severed the already ex-hausted bonds of professional solidarity: for this premature Darwinist, the confrère becomes the intimate enemy; before Hobbes he discovered the slogan of absolute competition: *Homo homini lupus.* Venice is up in arms. Unless a vaccine is discovered against the Tintoretto virus, it will dissolve the comfortable order of the guilds and leave behind nothing but a dust of antagonisms, of molecular solitudes. The Republic condemns these methods, labels them felonies, refers to work scamped, rebate sales, monopolies. Later, much later, other cities in another language will honor such procedures under the name of *struggle for existence, mass production, dumping, trust,* etc. For the moment, this shyster loses on one painting all that he makes on another. He carries off commissions at sword's point, but is often kept out of the market. By a strange reversal, it is this *native,* this hundred percent *Rialtino* who seems an intruder, almost an undesirable in his own city. The inevitable consequence is that he will go bankrupt unless he founds a family. First of all, to throttle rivalry in the studio itself; this champion of liberalism reverses the Biblical precept, making sure that others can never do unto him what he does unto them. Then too, he requires total approval;

ordinary apprentices might be frightened, discouraged by the widespread scandal surrounding him; how much time he would lose reassuring them! This thunderer will hurl only damp flashes from now on—what need has he of disciples? He wants extra hands, extra pairs of arms, nothing more. The road leads from absolute competition to family exploitation. In 1550 he marries Faustina dei Vescovi and immediately begins getting her with children. The same way he makes paintings: by tireless attack. And Faustina, a good layer, has only one flaw: she inclines to have too many daughters. So much the worse! Into the convent with them, all except for Marietta, whom he keeps in the house, and Ottavia, whom he marries off to a painter. He will get Faustina with child as often as necessary in order to wrench two sons from her, Domenico and Marco. But he has not waited for them to begin teaching the trade to his oldest daughter, Marietta. A woman painter in Venice is rare indeed: he must have been in a great hurry! Finally, around 1575, the operation seems to be complete: the new personnel consists of his son-in-law, Sebastiano Casser, Marietta, Domenico, and Marco. The symbol of a domestic association is the *domus* that shelters, that imprisons it. During the year, Jacopo buys a house. He will not leave it again. Here in his *lazaretto* the plaguestricken man will live in semiquarantine with his family, loving them the more for all *the others* outside who detest him. Considering him *at home,* in his work, in his relations with his wife and his children, we find he has an entirely different face: what a severe moralist! Perhaps a little Calvinistic around the edges? All the ingredients are there: pessimism and hard work, the spirit of lucre and family devotion. Human nature is corrupted by original sin; men are divided by interest. The Christian will be saved by works: let him struggle against the world; harsh with himself and others, let him travail without respite to em-bellish the earth God has entrusted to him; he will find the signs of Divine favor in the material success of his enterprise. As for the goodness of his heart, let him reserve that for the flesh of his flesh, for his sons. Was Venice affected by the Reformation? Assuredly, we find there, in the second half of the century, one Fra Paolo Sarpi, a curious individual who is extremely influential among the patricians, a friend of Galileo, hostile to Rome and in close though not clandestine communication with Protestant circles abroad. Yet if we can discern certain tendencies vaguely favorable to the Reformation on some intellectual levels, it is more than likely that the *petite bourgeoisie* was ignorant of them. Instead, we should say that the Most Serene Republic reformed itself. And long before this time: these merchants have been living on credit; they cannot accept the ban the Church has set upon those it persists in calling usurers; they favor science when it is practical and despise the Roman obscurantism; the Venetian state has always insisted on the preponderance of the civil authority: such is its doctrine, it is not to be revised. In all practical matters the state wields supreme control over its clergy, and when Pius the Fifth attempts to exempt ecclesiastics from the lay tribunals, the Senate flatly opposes him. For many reasons, moreover, the government regards the Holy See as a temporal and military rather than a spiritual power. Which does not keep the Republic, when its vital interests are at stake, from seeking a reconciliation with the Pope, from persecuting heretics or, to please his Most Christian Majesty, from organizing a sumptuous festival in honor of Saint Bartholomew. Tintoretto gets his crypto-Calvinism from his city itself: this painter unwittingly assimilates the incipient protestantism recognizable at the time in every great capitalist city.[3] The status of artists is quite equivocal at this period, particularly in Venice. But

---

3. The same that vaccinates the Italian towns against the Lutheran sickness and induces Italy to make its own religious revolution under the name of Counter-Reformation.

let us take our chances: perhaps this very ambiguity will help us understand Jacopo's melancholy puritan passion.

It has been said that "the Renaissance lent the artist the features which Antiquity attributed to the man of action and which the Middle Ages reserved for its saints."[4] This is not untrue, but the contrary observation seems to me at least as true: "In the sixteenth century painting and sculpture were still considered manual skills; all the honors were reserved for poetry; this accounts for the effort of the figurative arts to compete with literature."[5] There is certainly no doubt that Aretino, the poor man's Petronius, the rich man's Malaparte, was the arbiter of elegance and taste for the snobs of the Rialto, nor that Titian considered his friendship an honor: the painter needed every scrap of his immense fame to match the writer's status. And Michelangelo? He had the weakness of believing himself *well born,* and this illusion ruined his life. As a young man he might have hoped to study the humanities, to write: a noble deprived of a sword may fall back on the pen without lowering himself. He turned to the chisel from necessity and never got over it: Michelangelo formed his estimate of sculpture, of painting from the summit of his shame; his was the empty and shrunken joy of feeling superior to what he was doing. Compelled to silence, he attempted to provide the silent arts with language, to multiply allegories and symbols, writing a book on the Sistine ceiling, torturing marble to force it to speak.

Which then? Are the painters of the Renaissance hero-gods, or manual laborers? It all depends on how you look at it. It depends on the patrons, and on the manner of payment. Perhaps we can say they are manual laborers *first.* Afterwards, they become court employees or remain local masters. It is up to

---

4. Vuillemin, op. cit.
5. Eugenio Battista, in an excellent article on Michelangelo in *Epoca* (Aug. 25, 1957).

them to choose—or be chosen. Raphael and Michelangelo are
hirelings; they live in dependency and pride; one fall from
grace, however transitory, and they are out on the street; on
the other hand, the sovereign assumes responsibility for their
advertising. This sacred personage grants his elect a portion of
his own supernatural powers: the glory of the throne falls upon
them like a sunbeam, they reflect it upon the people; the divine
right of kings creates painters of the divine right. Thus a dauber
is transformed into a superman. After all, what are these *petits
bourgeois* some giant hand has snatched from the mob to hang
between heaven and earth, these satellites glittering with a
borrowed luster, if not men raised above humanity? Heroes—
meaning intercessors, intermediaries. Even today, our nostalgic
egalitarians worship in them, under the name of genius, the
light of that dead star, monarchy.

Tintoretto is the other kind: he works for merchants, for
officials, for parish churches. Not that he is uncultivated: he
was sent to school at seven, and left it at twelve, knowing how
to write and to count; and, above all, how can we refuse the
name of culture to that patient education of the senses, of the
hand and the mind, to that traditionalistic empiricism that, in
1530, studio painting still is? But Jacopo will never have
the apparatus of the courtier-painters. Michelangelo writes
sonnets; nowadays it is claimed that Raphael knew Latin;
association with intellectuals gave a certain gloss even to Titian
himself. In comparison with these worldlings, Tintoretto seems
an ignoramus: he will never have the time or taste for juggling
ideas or even words. He derides the humanism of the literati.
Venice has few poets, still fewer philosophers: for him, there
are already too many, he frequents none of them. Not that
he avoids them—he ignores them. He concedes their social
superiority; Aretino may congratulate him with all the condescension of a protector: this celebrated figure is *received*, he
is part of society, aristocrats invite him to their tables who

would not dream of even greeting a painter in the street. But must he be envied into the bargain? Must he be envied *because he writes?* For Jacopo the mind's creations look distinctly gratuitous and thereby wicked: God has put us on earth to earn our bread by the sweat of our brow; writers do not sweat. Do they even work? Jacopo never opens a book save for his missal; the preposterous notion of abusing his talent to compete with literature would never occur to him: we can find everything in his pictures, but they never try to *say* anything, they are mute as the world itself. This artisan's son respects only physical effort, only manual creation. What he likes about the painter's trade is that a man's professional skill can be carried to the point of prestidigitation, the delicacy of the merchandise to its culmination. The artist is the supreme workman: he exhausts himself and the material to produce and to sell . . . visions.

This would not keep him from working for the princes if he liked them. He does not like them, that is the heart of the matter: they frighten without inspiring him. He has never tried to approach them nor to make himself known: it is as if he were trying to confine his fame within the walls of Venice. So far as we know, he never leaves the city save for one excursion, at the age of sixty, to nearby Mantua. And then he has to be begged: asked to come and hang his canvases himself, he announces he will not budge unless he can bring his wife along. This stipulation is a credit to his conjugal sentiments, but reveals still more about his dislike of traveling. And we must not assume that his Venetian colleagues resemble him in this: they gallop the roads of Europe as, a hundred years before, Gentile Bellini sailed the seas. What adventurers! Tintoretto is a mole: he is comfortable only in the narrow galleries of his burrow. Whenever he thinks of the world, he has an attack of agoraphobia; still, if he must choose, he prefers to risk his neck rather than his pictures. He accepts foreign commissions—and for him the world starts to be foreign in Padua—but does not solicit them. What a contrast between his frenzy in the Doges' Palace, at the Scuola San Rocco, at the *Crociferi,* and this indifference! He shifts responsibility for the work's execution onto his assistants, oversees these ready-made productions at a distance, makes sure not to touch them with his own hand, as if he feared risking the smallest wisp of his talent outside his country: Europe is entitled to nothing but B pictures. In the Prado, the National Gallery, the Louvre, in Munich, in Vienna, in the Vatican, you can find Raphael, Titian, a hundred others. All, or almost all, save Tintoretto. Jacopo Robusti has fiercely saved himself for his fellow citizens, and you will learn nothing about him unless you look for him in his native city, for the good reason that he never wanted to leave it.

But we must be exact. For in Venice itself he had some two hundred different patrons at his disposal. He paints the seat of government, and of course, when the Senate commissions him, the entire studio falls to work, including the head of the family. In the Doges' Palace, where the lighting shows them at their best, you can see today the works of a powerful collective personality bearing the name Tintoretto. But if it is Jacopo Robusti who interests you, leave the Piazzetta, cross the Piazza San Marco, cross the donkey-back bridges over the canals, thread a maze of dark alleys, and go into some even darker church: he is there. In the Scuola San Rocco, you have him: in person, without Marietta or Domenico or Sebastiano Casser; here he works alone. A leaden mist dulls the canvases, or there is a glare that keeps you from seeing them properly; be patient until your eyes grow accustomed to the light, or rather the darkness, and finally you will see a rose in the gloom, a genius in the shadow. And who has paid for *these* paintings? Sometimes the parishioners, sometimes the members of the Guild: the bourgeois, *grand* and *petit* alike; this is his true public, the only one he loves.

This painter-shopkeeper has nothing about him of the hero-god. With a little luck he will be notorious, even famous; glorious, never: his profane clientele is not qualified to consecrate him. Of course, the celebrity of his august colleagues honors the entire profession: he too gleams a little. Does he yearn for their glory? Perhaps. But he does none of the things necessary to acquire it; devil take the favor of princes: it enslaves. Jacopo Robusti is proud of staying a small-time employer, a fine-arts salesman paid on commission, a master in his own house. He makes no distinction between the producer's economic independence and the artist's freedom; his dealings prove he vaguely hopes to reverse the market, control demand by supply: has he not slowly, patiently created in the brothers of San Rocco a need for art—a certain art—which he alone can satisfy? His autonomy is all the better preserved since he works for collectivities—associations, parishes—and since these large bodies reach their decisions by a majority vote.

Michelangelo, a phony noble, and Titian, a son of the peasantry, succumb at once to the lure of the monarchy. Tintoretto, however, is born in a society of worker-employers; the artisan is an amphibian: as a manual laborer, he is proud of his hands; as a *petit bourgeois,* it is the *grande bourgeoisie* that attracts him: this is the class which by the mere fact of competition assures the interior of a stifling protectionism a degree of ventilation. At this period, there was a *bourgeois hope* in Venice. A slender hope; the aristocracy had long since taken its precautions: in this stratified universe, though you may *become* rich, you must be *born* a patrician; besides, even wealth is limited: not only are the businessman, the industrialist confined to their class, but are long forbidden the more lucrative trades; the State accords the *appalto*—the renting of galleys— to the aristocrats alone. Scheming and melancholy *bourgeoisie!* Everywhere else in Europe, it betrays itself, buys titles and castles as soon as it can. In Venice, it is denied everything, even the modest fortunes of treason. So it must betray in dreams. La Giovita Fontana, from Piacenza, sets up in business, makes money, and spends it on a palace on the Grand Canal; in these few words lies a whole life: a fierce desire, once satisfied, ultimately turns into ambitious snobbery, a tradeswoman dies and is resuscitated in the form of an imaginary aristocrat. The self-made rich go around in circles, conceal their fantasies; grouped in guilds, they spend their money on works of charity, their melancholy austerity contrasting with the melancholy orgies of a disenchanted aristocracy.

For the Republic is no longer queen of the seas, gradually the aristocracy declines, the bankruptcies multiply, the number of impoverished noblemen rises, while the rest have lost the spirit of enterprise: these ship-owners' sons buy land, become *rentiers*. Already, mere "citizens" replace them in certain positions; galleys pass into bourgeois hands, under bourgeois command. The *bourgeoisie* is still far from considering itself as a rising class; it occurs to no one that one day it might replace the decaying nobility: let us say, rather, that the bourgeoisie is a prey to an obscure agitation that makes its condition less supportable and resignation more difficult.

Tintoretto does not dream. Ever. If men's ambition is measured by the aperture of their social future, the most ambitious commoners in Venice are the *petits bourgeois,* for they can still raise themselves above their class. But our painter feels profound affinities with his clients: he appreciates their love of work, their probity, their practicality; he enjoys their nostalgia and, above all, he shares their profound aspiration: all, if only to produce, if only to buy and sell—all need freedom. These are the keys of Tintoretto's *arrivisme*: it is a gasp for an air from the heights. Disturbances in heaven, a distant, invisible ascension, open a vertical future and this bottle imp rises, a draft sucks him upward, the new spirit penetrates him: since childhood, he has thought *en bourgeois*. But the contradictions of his native class will limit his ambitions: as an executive, he wants to cross the line; as a laborer he insists on working with his own hands. This is enough to indicate his place. There are— approximately—7,600 patricians in Venice, 13,600 citizens, 127,000 artisans, workers, and small businessmen, 12,900 servants, and 550 beggars. Not counting Jews and nobles, beggars and servants, Tintoretto has eyes only for the ideal demarcation that separates the commoners into two groups: 13,600 on one side, 127,000 on the other; he wants to be the first among the latter, the last among the former: in short, the humblest of the rich, and the most distinguished of their purveyors. This makes this artisan, buried in an anxious Venice, a false bourgeois, truer than the true ones. In him, and on his canvases, the brotherhood of San Rocco enjoy the ideal image of a *bourgeoisie* that does not betray itself.

Even when he works for the Sovereign Pontiff, Michelangelo believes he is lowering himself; such disdain gives him an occasional perspective: this gentleman can afford to be flippant about art. Tintoretto is quite the opposite, he transcends himself only as a painter; without art, what would he be? A dyer. Art is the force that wrenches him from his natal condition and the milieu which supports it, art is his dignity. He must work or sink back down in the bottle. Perspective? Long views? Where would he find them? He has no time to cross-examine himself about painting—who knows if he even sees it? Michelangelo thinks too much: he is a Marquis de Carabas, an intellectual; Tintoretto doesn't know what he is doing: he paints.

So much for his *arrivisme:* this artist's fate is to incarnate bourgeois puritanism in a declining aristocratic Republic. Elsewhere, this somber humanism would prevail; in Venice, it will disappear without even becoming conscious of itself, but not without wakening the suspicion and the hostility of an aristocracy always on the alert. The sullenness official and bureaucratic Venice manifests toward Tintoretto is the same the patricians express with regard to the Venetian *bourgeoisie*. These wrangling merchants and their painter are a threat to the Most Serene Order: they must be kept under observation.

3. *The Fugitive*

We may discern a certain arrogance in the persistent refusal to compete: "I acknowledge no rival, I admit no judge." Michelangelo might say that. The unfortunate thing is that Tintoretto does not say that. Quite the contrary: when he is invited to submit a sketch he eagerly accepts. Afterwards, we know he tosses his thunderbolt. Rather the way an octopus squirts its ink. The thunderbolt dazzles, the spectators cannot see his picture; besides, everything is arranged so that they never need to look at it or, above all, to appreciate it: when the lightning fades, the canvas is hung, the gift registered, only the flash of fire will have been seen. Unless I am entirely wrong, Jacopo is begging the question; it is as if he were afraid to confront his adversaries. Would he deploy all this ingenuity if he were certain that talent alone would prevail? Would he deign to astonish his contemporaries by the quantity of his production if they unreservedly admired its quality?

Then too, this rage to prevail by parading himself is more striking in competition: but that is his style, his universal signature: the least comparison or even contiguity offends him. In 1559, San Rocco commissions him to paint *Saint Mark Healing the Paralytic* to match a canvas by Pordenone. No one asks him to imitate his predecessor's manner; no contest[6] can oppose the two painters; Antonio di Sacchis has been dead for twenty years; even if he had once been able to influence his junior, the time of influence is over: Jacopo is the master of his art. Yet he cannot help it, he must "make" a Pordenone;

---

6. Ridolfi, deceived by the similarity of styles, says the work was painted "*in concurrenza con il Pordenone.*"

it has been pointed out just how he "exaggerates the baroque violence of the gestures . . . by the conflict between the monumental figures and the architecture in which they are so closely wedged," how he "has produced this effect by lowering the ceiling . . . and by [using] the columns themselves . . . to freeze the gestures, to paralyze their violence."[7] In other words, he trembles at the notion of imprisoning himself forever in an inert confrontation: "Compare Pordenone with Pordenone, if you want to; as for Jacopo Robusti, I'm off duty." He has managed matters, of course, so that the false Di Sacchis utterly overpowers the real one. His withdrawal is not a defeat; he leaves a challenge behind him as he goes: "The old, the new— I take them all on, and beat them at their own game." But here is precisely what we find suspect: why should he play *their* game, abide by *their* rules, when he need only be himself to triumph over them? How much resentment in his insolence— this Cain assassinates every Abel preferred to him: "You like Veronese? All right, I can surpass him if I deign to imitate him; you think he's a man when he's only a method." And how much humility too: occasionally this rejected creature slips into someone else's skin to experience for himself the solace of being loved. And sometimes it is as if he lacked the courage to manifest his scandalous genius; exhausted, he leaves it in half-darkness and attempts to prove it by arguing *ab absurdo:* "Since I paint the best Veronese and the best Pordenone, imagine *what I could do* if I were to be myself!" Actually, he almost never permits himself to do this unless someone shows confidence in him first and leaves every wall of an empty hall to him alone. Such an attitude originates, of course, in the hostility that has been shown toward him. But the painter's timidity and the prejudices of his fellow citizens derive from one and the same malaise: in 1548, in Venice, under Tintoretto's brush, before

7. Vuillemin, op. cit., p. 1974. Cf. also Ietze, p. 372, and Newton, p. 72.

the patricians, the art lovers and the town wits, *painting grows frightened of itself.*

A long evolution has begun, which will everywhere substitute the profane for the sacred: cold, sparkling with crystals, the various branches of human activity will rise, one after the other, from the sweet bath of divine promiscuity. Art is affected: out of a last wisp of fog emerges that sumptuous disenchantment, painting. It still recalls the period when Duccio or Giotto showed God the Creation as it had come from His hands: once He had recognized His work, the transaction was in the bag and the world in a frame, for eternity. Between the painting and the supreme Eye, monks and prelates occasionally and transparently glided on tiptoe, to look at what God himself was looking at, and when they went away they apologized for the intrusion. All is over: the Eye is closed, Heaven blind. What has happened? First of all, a change in clientele: so long as artists painted for clerics, all was well; from the day when the greatest of the Florentine bankers had the preposterous notion of decorating the walls of his house with frescoes, the Almighty, disgusted, retired to his detached role as Amateur of Souls. Then too, there occurred that Florentine adventure, the conquest of perspective. Perspective is profane, sometimes even a profanation: consider Mantegna's supine Christ, his feet in the foreground, his head anyhow; who can suppose the Heavenly Father will tolerate a foreshortened Son? God is absolute proximity, the universal presence of Love: can He be shown *from a distance* the Universe *He* has created and which He refrains from annihilating at every moment? Is it for Being to conceive and create Non-Being? for the Absolute to engender the Relative? for the Light to contemplate the Shadows? for Reality to take itself for an appearance? No; it is the eternal story that begins all over again: curiosity, the Tree of Knowledge, Original Sin and the Expulsion. This time the apple is called "perspective." But the Adamites of Florence nibble at it instead of eating it, which keeps them from discovering their fall at once: in the middle of the *quattrocento,* Uccello still imagines himself in Paradise, and poor Alberti, theoretician of the "perspectivists," is still offering geometrical optics as an Ontology of Visibility; he retains enough ingenuousness, in other words, to insist that the Divine Regard stands surety for a vanishing point. Heaven grants no satisfaction to this absurd request: creation is immediately relegated to its own nothingness, which it rediscovers all over again; distance, removal, separation: such negations mark our limits; only man has a horizon. Alberti's window opens on a measurable universe, but this rigorous miniature depends entirely upon the point that defines our station and our dispersion: depends on our eye. In his *Annunciation,* between the Angel and the Virgin, Piero della Francesca sets a perspective of columns: this is only an appearance; in themselves and for their creator, all alike and all incomparable, these inert whitenesses have not stopped sleeping: perspective is a violence human weakness works upon God's microcosm. A hundred years later, in the Netherlands, Being will be rediscovered at the heart of Seeming, and appearance will resume its dignity as apparition: painting will have new aims, will find a new meaning. But before Vermeer can give us the sky and the stars, day and night, the moon and the earth in the shape of a little brick wall, the bourgeois of the North must win their great victories and forge their humanism.

In the sixteenth century, in Italy, artists still burn with faith, they muster eye and hand to join battle against atheism. To embrace the Absolute more closely, they have perfected techniques that cast them into a relativism they detest. These mystified dogmatists can neither advance nor retreat. If God no longer looks at the images they paint, who will bear witness for them? They show man his own impotence: where will he find the strength to guarantee them? Then too, if painting has no purpose save to measure our myopia, it is not worth an hour of effort. Showing man to the Almighty who condescended to raise him from the slime was an act of thanksgiving, a sacrifice. But showing him to man—why bother? Why show him *as he is not?* The *fin-de-siècle* artists—those born around 1480—Titian, Giorgione, Raphael, find ways of compromising with Heaven. We shall come back to them. Then too, the wealth and power of the means still conceals the sinister indetermination of the ends. Still, we may presume that Raphael has some presentiment of this when he gives everything up, goes whoring every night, sells chromos and incites his assistants, out of *Schadenfreude,* to make obscene engravings: he is a suicide of facility. In any case, the painter's happiness vanished with these sacred monsters. In the second quarter of the century, painting went mad, alienated by its own perfection. In the barbarous taste of the period for the great "realizations" we discern a sickness: the public insists that all the pomps of realism be used to conceal its subjectivity: the creator must efface himself before life, must make himself *forgotten;* it would be best if we could come on paintings by surprise, somewhere in the woods, and the figures in them, wrenching themselves from the canvas among the splinters of a broken frame, should spring at the throats of the passers-by. The object must reabsorb its visibility, must contain it within itself, must distract attention by a continuous appeal to all the senses and particularly to the sense of touch; everything must function to replace *representation* with the spectator's secret participation in the scene, horror and sympathy must hurl men into conflict with their simulacra, and if it is at all possible, desire, burning all the torches of perspective, must reveal that *ersatz* of divine ubiquity, the immediate presence of the flesh; the eye's Reason may be respected, but the heart has its reasons which must oppose them. What is wanted is the *thing itself* and irresistible: larger than life, more immediate and more beautiful: this is Terrorism. But terrorism is a disease of Rhetoric. Shamed, art must go into hiding when it has lost its letters of credit. Bound, spied on, subject to the checks of State, Church, and taste, more circumscribed, perhaps more honored than ever before, the artist, for the first time in history, becomes conscious of his solitude. Who has sanctioned him? Where does this right he assumes come from? Night has fallen. God has gone out: how paint at night? And for *whom?* And *what?* And *why?* Art's subject remains the *world,* an absolute: but reality escapes, the ascension from finite to infinite is reversed. A great plenitude once supported the misery and weakness of bodies; now this weakness becomes the only plenitude, the unique security: the Infinite is the void, the darkness within creation and outside it; the Absolute is absence. God takes refuge in souls: He is the desert. It is too late to *show,* too soon to *shout;* the painter is in hell, and what is born is a new damnation: genius, for genius is this uncertainty, this mad desire to pass through the Dark Night of the World and contemplate it from outside, to splash it on walls, on canvas, by sweeping it with unheard-of beams of light. Genius, a new word in Europe, a conflict of the relative with the absolute, of a limited presence with an infinite absence. For the painter knows he will not leave this world; and even if he could, he would carry this piercing nothingness every-where: you cannot transcend perspective so long as you have not granted yourself the right to create another plastic space.

Michelangelo dies obsessed, summing up his despair and his scorn in these two words: original sin. Tintoretto says nothing; he cheats: if he were to admit his solitude, he could not endure it. Naturally he suffers from it more than anyone: this false bourgeois who works for bourgeois patrons hasn't even the alibi of glory. This is the viper's tangle: the Little Dyer wriggles in the toils of that personality neurosis Henri Jeanson so aptly calls "the terrifying moral health of the ambitious"; he assigns himself modest goals: to raise himself above his father by the judicious exploitation of his gifts, to corner the market by flattering the tastes of the public. A cheerful *arrivisme* seasoned with *savoir-faire,* promptness and talent—nothing is missing and everything is spoiled by one dizzying lacuna, by an Art without God. This Art is ugly, wicked, nocturnal; it is the imbecile longing of the part for the whole. Lured by the void, Jacopo rushes off on a motionless journey from which he will never return.

Genius does not exist: it is the shamefaced audacity of nothingness; the Little Dyer exists, though, and knows his limits: he is sensible enough to believe in darning. All he asks is a modest plenitude: what has he to do with the infinite? And how should he know that his slightest brushstroke is enough to challenge his judges? His stubborn and shabby ambition would unravel in the Night of Unknowing. It is not his fault, after all, if painting is a lost dog without a collar: later, there will be madmen to rejoice in their destitution; in the middle of the sixteenth century, the first victim of monocular perspective tries to conceal his. Working alone and for nothing means to die of fear. He must have arbiters. At all costs. A prize jury. God has fallen silent, Venice remains: Venice that stuffs holes, fills pockets, blocks exits, stops hemorrhages, cuts off all escapes. In the Doges' Republic, good citizens are accountable to the State for all their activities; if they happen to paint, they must decorate the city. Jacopo hands himself over to his fellow citizens; they have a certain extremely academic notion of art, which he eagerly adopts. Particularly since it always has been his as well, repeated from his earliest childhood until he has come to believe it: the artisan's worth is measured by the number and importance of his commissions and the value of the honors paid him. So he will conceal his genius beneath his *arrivisme* and regard social success as the only outward sign of the mystical victory. His bad faith is obvious; on earth he plays solitaire and cheats; and then there are the dice he casts into the face of Heaven without cheating: yet if he wins here below with all these aces he pulls out of his sleeve, he dares to claim his victory on high; if he sells his canvases, it is because he has ensnared the world. But who can blame him for his gross cunning? It is the nineteenth century that decreed the divorce between artist and public; in the sixteenth, it is *true* that paint- ing goes mad: it has ceased to be a religious sacrifice; but it is *no less true* that it becomes rational: it remains a social serv- ice. Who in Venice would dare say: "I paint for myself, I am my own witness"? And are we so sure that those who say it today are not lying? Everyone is a judge, no one is a judge: content yourself with that. Tintoretto seems more unfortunate than guilty: his art rends the age like a white-hot blade, but he can see it only with the eyes of his time. The fact remains that he has chosen his own hell: instantly the finite closes over the infinite, ambition over genius, Venice over her painter, who will not emerge again. But the captive infinite taints everything: Jacopo's rational *arrivisme* turns to frenzy: once it was merely a question of making good, now he must *prove*. A voluntary defendant, the wretch has committed himself to an endless trial; he will assume his own defense, make each painting a witness in his behalf; he pleads, he never stops pleading: there is a city to convince, here are its magistrates, its bourgeois who, alone and conclusively, will decide his mortal future and his immortality as well. Yet it is Jacopo and only Jacopo who has produced this strange amalgam; he must choose: to be his own recourse by legislating without appeal or transform the Most Serene Republic into an absolute tribunal. Under these con- ditions, he made the only choice he could. Unfortunately for him. How well I understand his indifference toward the rest of the universe! What need has he of German or even Florentine approval! Venice is the richest, the most beautiful city in the world, it has the best painters, the best critics, the most enlightened amateurs and collectors: it is *here* he must play his game, each move forever; without once flinching; it is here, in brick alleys between a thin strip of sky and the stagnant water, under the flamboyant absence of the sun, that Eternity will be won or lost in a single life, forever.

So be it, we say. But why cheat? Why dress up in Veronese's feathers? If it is by his genius that he wants to dazzle us, why smother it so often? And why assent to judges if it is only to corrupt and dupe them?

Why? Because the tribunal is forewarned, the case lost, the verdict rendered, and because he knows it. In 1548 he asks Venice to guarantee the infinite; the city is frightened, and refuses. What a fate! Abandoned by God, he must cheat to find his judges; and once he has found them, he must cheat to get his trial postponed. He spends his life keeping them in suspense, sometimes running away, sometimes turning back upon them in order to blind them. Everything is here: the pain and the peevishness, the arrogance, the expedience, the rage, the rancor, the implacable pride and the abject desire to be loved. Tintoretto's painting is above all a love affair between a man and a city.

4. *A Mole in the Sunlight*

In this story of madmen, the city seems even crazier than the man. She has honored all her painters: why show this one, the greatest of them all, such grudging suspicion, such sullenness? Quite simply, because she loves another.

The Most Serene Republic is hungry for prestige: her ships have long been her glory; exhausted, somewhat fallen, she hangs her pride upon an artist. Titian is worth a fleet in himself: he has stolen flakes of fire from crowns and tiaras to weave himself an aureole. His adopted country admires in him *above all* the respect he inspires in the Emperor: in the sacred light, still terrible but quite harmless, which plays about this head she claims to recognize her own glory. The painter of kings cannot help being the king of painters: the Queen of the Seas adopts him and thereby recovers something of her majesty; once she gave him a trade, a reputation, but when he works now the divine right penetrates the walls and gleams as far as San Marco, and she knows he has returned what he received from her a hundredfold: he is a National Capital. Furthermore, this man has the longevity of trees, he lasts a century, and gradually transforms himself into a corporation. The presence of this academy with only one member, born before them and apparently determined to outlast them, demoralizes the young, exasperates and discourages their ambitions: they suppose that their city has the power to immortalize the living and that she has reserved this favor for Titian alone. A victim of this misunderstanding, Tintoretto—under the fallacious pretext: "I'm as good as he is"—insists he be made the equal of his illustrious predecessor. But worth has nothing to do with the case: we do not ask of republics what rightfully belongs to hereditary monarchies. Jacopo is wrong to reproach his city for expending all her wattage on the baobab of the Rialto; the spotlights are in Rome or in Madrid, outside the walls in any case, focused on this old trunk and incidentally wresting Venice from her shadows; the city's illumination is indirect. And I was wrong too, when I thought of calling this section: "In Titian's shadow." For *Titian casts no shadow*. Let us remember this: at Jacopo's birth the old man is forty-one; he is seventy-two when his junior makes his first attempt to assert his powers. This would be the moment to move aside, there would be something becoming about dying now. Nothing of the kind! This unkillable monarch has another twenty-seven years to reign. When, at a hundred, he finally disappears, he has the last good fortune to leave an unfinished *Pietà,* like some young hopeful cut down before his time. For more than half a century,

Tintoretto-the-Mole scampers through a labyrinth whose walls are splashed and splattered with Titian's glory; until the age of fifty-eight, this nocturnal creature is pursued by the floodlights, blinded by the implacable celebrity of Another. When this brilliance is turned off at last, Jacopo Robusti is quite old enough to be dead. He manages to survive the tyrant, but to no avail: Titian's genius was to combine two contradictory functions, to become a Court employee while retaining the independence of a small businessman; this fortunate conjuncture is not often encountered in history. Certainly we are far from it with Tintoretto, who has put all his eggs in one basket. Go look at the two tombs: you will find out what it costs him even today to have prepared his country for everything. The Old Man's radioactive corpse has been buried under a mountain of lard in Santa Maria dei Frari, virtually a cemetery of Doges; Tintoretto's body rests under a slab in the dim penumbra of a neighborhood church. Speaking for myself, I think this is an ideal arrangement; let Titian have the lard, the sugar and the caramels: they are his poetic deserts, and I should have been even more pleased had he been buried under the Victor Emmanuel monument in Rome, the most hideous in Italy after the railroad station in Milan; for Jacopo, the honors of naked stone: his name is enough. But since this opinion is strictly personal, I should understand if an irritated traveler were to ask Venice for an accounting: "Ungrateful city, is this all you could do for the best of your sons? Niggardly city, why set footlights in front of Titian's opera *The Assumption* and begrudge electricity to Robusti's canvases?" I know Venice's answer: it can be found in Aretino's correspondence for 1599: "If Robusti wants to be honored, why doesn't he paint like Vecellio?" Jacopo will hear this refrain all the days of his life, and after his death as before it. It is still repeated today: "Where is he heading? Why wander from the Royal Way, since he's lucky enough to find it traced for him? Our great Vecellio has carried

painting to such heights of perfection that it must not be tam-
pered with: either newcomers will follow in the Master's footsteps or Art will fall back into barbarism." Capricious Venetians! Inconsistent bourgeois! Tintoretto is *their* painter; he
shows them what they see, what they feel; they cannot endure
him; Titian mocks them: they adore him. Titian spends the better part of his life tranquilizing princes, proving in his pictures
that all's for the best in the best of all possible worlds. Discord is
but an appearance, the worst enemies are secretly reconciled by
the colors of their cloaks. Violence? A ballet danced without too
much conviction by phony toughs with silken beards: here is
the justification of wars! The painter's art turns to apologetics,
becomes Theodicy: suffering, injustice, and evil do not exist;
nor mortal sin: Adam and Eve fall only to learn, and to teach
us, that they were naked—in a great, four-branched gesture,
God noble and indolent, bending down from the height of
Heaven, and Man leaning over backward, stretching out his
arms. Order prevails: mastered, enslaved, perspective respects
hierarchies; discrete compromises reserve the best seats for
kings, for saints. If someone wanders off into the wasteland
distance, lit by the smoky lamps of a bad neighborhood, it is
never by chance: this gloom corresponds to the obscurity of
his condition; besides, we must burnish the foreground's brilliance by contrast. The brush pretends to narrate an event and
instead recalls a ceremony; sacrificing movement to order and
relief to unity, it caresses bodies more than it models them; out
of all the graybeards who applaud the Assumption, not one
exists independently: the group comes first, its arms raised, its
legs bristling: a burning bush; after which the substance assumes some diversity by producing those provisional figures
which scarcely stand out from the collective background and
which it can reabsorb at any moment: such is the condition of
the common man; Titian saves individuality for the Great,
though he is careful to round off any sharp edges: relief isolates,

removes, it is a pessimism; the courtier, an optimist by condition, first indicates, then irons smooth his individuals and uses all the colors of the rainbow to sing the glory of God. Then he begins licking his canvas smooth: erasures and polishings, lacquers and veneers. He spares no effort to conceal his work and ends by conjuring himself out of the picture; we enter an empty painting, we walk through flowers, under a perfect sun, the owner is dead; we are so much alone that we forget ourselves and vanish, and what remains is the greatest betrayal of all: Beauty.

For once, the traitor has the excuse of believing in what he does: Titian is not a city man, but a *parvenu* peasant; when he arrives in Venice he comes from the country and from childhood, from the depths of the Middle Ages. This earth-stained rustic has long nursed a reverential love for the lords: he rises through the *bourgeoisie* without even noticing it and joins his true masters in heaven, all the surer of pleasing them since he respects them so sincerely. It is often said that he secretly considers himself their equal: I do not believe this can be so. Where would such light have come from? He is a vassal: ennobled by the glory that kings and kings alone can shed, he owes them everything, even his pride: why should he turn it against them? His insolent fortune, the hierarchy of powers and the beauty of the world are to him merely a reciprocity of reflections; with the best faith in the world, he puts the bourgeois techniques of the Renaissance at the service of feudalism: he has stolen the tool.

Yet bourgeois and patricians admire him equally: he gives an alibi to the technocrats of Venice: he tells of happiness, glory, and pre-established harmony just when they are making the most commendable efforts to conceal their collapse from themselves. Every merchant—whether noble or commoner—is enchanted by these smug canvases that reflect the quietude of kings. If everything is for the best, if evil is merely a splendid appearance, if each man is eternally fixed in his hereditary place in the divine and social hierarchy, then nothing has happened in the last hundred years: the Turks have not taken Constantinople, Columbus has not discovered America, the Portuguese have not plotted to form a coalition against the Most Serene Republic. People had only imagined that the Barbary pirates held the seas, that the African sources of precious metals had been exhausted, that the scarcity of money during the first half of the century had retarded trade, only imagined that suddenly the Peruvian gold, flowing torrentially from the Spanish reservoir, had changed everything, stimulated a rise in prices, flooded the market: it was all a dream; Venice still rules the Mediterranean, she is at the peak of her power, her wealth, her greatness. In other words, these anxiety-ridden men want Beauty because it is reassuring. I can understand them: I have taken some two hundred plane trips without getting used to it; I'm too old a biped to find flying normal; sometimes—particularly when my fellow passengers are as ugly as myself—my fear awakens; yet if only one pretty woman, a handsome boy or a charming couple in love is on board, my fear vanishes; ugliness is a prophecy: in it there is a kind of extremism that tries to carry negation to the point of horror. The Beautiful seems indestructible; its sacred image protects us: so long as it remains among us, the catastrophe will not occur. This is the case in Venice: the city begins to fear collapsing into the slime of its lagoons; it imagines it can escape through Beauty, that supreme frivolity; it claims to make buoys and lifebelts of its palaces and its frescoes. Those who assure Titian's success are the same men who desert the sea, who shun disenchantment in orgies, who prefer the security of ownership to the profits of trade.

Tintoretto is born in a ravaged city; he has breathed the Venetian anxiety all his life, it obsesses him, it is all he can paint. If they were in his position, his severest critics would not do otherwise. But precisely—they are *not* in his position: they

cannot help feeling this anxiety, but they do not want anyone
to show it to them; they condemn the pictures that represent it.
Bad luck has doomed Jacopo to make himself—unconsciously
—the witness of a period which refuses to know itself. Here
we discover at a glance the meaning of his fate and the secret of
the Venetian grudge. Tintoretto displeases everyone: the
patricians, because he reveals the puritanism and the brooding
agitation of the bourgeois; the artisans, because he destroys the
corporative order and betrays, beneath an apparent professional solidarity, the stirring of factions and rivalries; the
patriots, because the excesses of the painting and the absence
of God reveal, beneath his brush, an absurd and chance world
where anything can happen, *even* the death of Venice. At least,
then, this painter-turned-bourgeois pleases his adoptive class?
Far from it! The *bourgeoisie* does not accept him unreservedly;
he fascinates always, but often alarms. This is because the Venetian *bourgeoisie* is not conscious of itself. Messire di Zigninoni
doubtless dreamed of betraying; obscurely he sought a way of
joining the aristocracy—in short, of escaping that bourgeois
reality he helped create in spite of himself: what most disturbs
him about Robusti's pictures is their radicalism and their dis-
intoxicating, demystifying virtues. In other words, this evidence
must be challenged at any cost, Tintoretto's effort must be
presented as a failure, the originality of his experiments must
be denied—*get rid of this man.*

Consider, then, what he is blamed for: first, for working too
fast and for letting his hand show everywhere; what is wanted
is something licked smooth, something finished, above all something *impersonal:* if the painter reveals himself, he questions
himself; if he questions himself, he puts his audience in question;
Venice imposes on her artists the puritan maxim: "No personal
remarks"; she will be careful to identify Jacopo's lyricism with
the haste of an overtaxed purveyor who scamps his work. Then
too, there is Ridolfi's gossip; Tintoretto supposedly wrote on the

wall of his studio: "Titian's color and Michelangelo's modeling." This is idiotic: we first find the formula in 1548, from
the pen of a Venetian art critic without any reference to Robusti.
As a matter of fact, the latter can only have known Michelangelo's works through the reproductions of Daniele de
Volterra: in other words, at the *earliest* in 1557. And what do
we take him for? Can we believe he would seriously devote
himself to concocting this absurd potion? As a matter of fact, it
is a daydream of the period: in the face of the Spanish peril, the
cities of northern and central Italy dream of uniting forces, too
late. But the stirring of a national conscience quickly lulled
back to sleep still exerts its temporary influence on the fine arts.
"Michelangelo and Titian" means Florence and Venice—once
unified, how beautiful painting would become!

   Nothing serious, of course; this dream is harmless so long
as everyone dreams it. But those who claim to see in it *only*
Robusti's obsession must have hoped to ruin this artist by lodg-
ing an explosive nightmare at the very core of his art. Color
is man smiling; modeling, man in tears. Here unity, there a
permanent danger of anarchy. On the one hand, the harmony
of the spheres; on the other, destitution. The two titans of the
century hurl themselves on one another, each trying to gain
a stranglehold, and Jacopo is the theatre of operations. And
sometimes Titian gets the upper hand by a hairsbreadth; sometimes, agonizingly, Michelangelo prevails. Always the loser
retains enough strength to spoil the winner's triumph: the result of this Pyrrhic victory is a spoiled picture. Spoiled by excess:
Tintoretto looks to his contemporaries like a Titian gone mad,
devoured by Buonarotti's morbid passion, shaken by Saint
Vitus's dance. A case of possession, a freak schizophrenia. In
one sense, Jacopo does not exist save on a battlefield; in another,
he is a monster, a defection. Vasari's fable takes on a singular
meaning: Adam Robusti wanted to taste the fruits of the Tree
of Knowledge, and the Archangel Tiziano, finger pointing,

wings beating, drove him out of paradise. To have bad luck or to carry it is the same thing in Italy, even today. After financial difficulties, an automobile accident, a broken leg, if your wife has recently left you—don't expect to be asked to dinner: a hostess will not readily expose her other guests to precocious baldness, a cold in the head, or, in extreme cases, to a broken neck on her stairs. I know one Milanese who has the evil eye; this came to light last year: he hasn't a single friend left and cooks for himself, at home. Jacopo is that kind of man: a bearer of misfortune because misfortune has been cast upon him. Or, perhaps, on his mother when she bore him. But the truth is, the *gettatura* comes from Venice: anxious, damned, the city has produced a man of anxiety, and in him damns her own. The wretch loves despairingly a city in despair, a city that cannot bear to accept him, for such love horrifies its object. When Tintoretto passes, it is best to get out of the way: he smells of death. Which is perfectly true. But what else do they smell of, the patrician festivals, the bourgeois charity and the docility of the people? And the pink houses with their flooded cellars, their walls riddled by rats? What do they smell of, the stagnant canals with their urinal watercress, their gray mussels stuck to the quays with a squalid putty? At the bottom of a *rio* there is a bubble fastened to the clay, the eddies of the gondolas detach it, it rises through the filthy water, touches the surface, turns, sparkles, bursts, leaving a ring, and everything bursts with it: the bourgeois nostalgia, the greatness of the Republic, God, and Italian painting.

Tintoretto has been in mourning for Venice and for a world; yet when he dies no one puts on mourning for him and then there is silence; hypocritically pious hands have hung his canvases with crepe. Tear away this black veil, and we shall find a portrait, begun a hundred times over. Jacopo's? That of the Adriatic's bride? As you please: the city and her painter have one and the same face.

FROM The Dreamer, a comedy*

by JEAN VAUTHIER

English version by URSULE MOLINARO and
VENABLE HERNDON

CAST OF CHARACTERS

LAURETTE, Simon's wife. Pretty. About thirty years old.
SIMON, Strong and full of energy. In the prime of life.
GEORGE, Frail young man, sensitive, scrupulous. Twenty-six.
MR. MANASSÉ, Businessman.

(George has come to tell Laurette and Simon about his
dream.)

LAURETTE. . . . What were you saying, George? Have you
    told your dream? Is it a pretty dream? Will it make me
    laugh?
    [*Without transition.*]
GEORGE [*gets up and, with great sincerity*]. . . . Well, it was
    a marvelous night / and pierced with lights . . . many—
    many, many small lights blinking endlessly, before me, every-
    where————blinking by the thousands.

* CAUTION: All rights, including professional, amateur, motion-picture,
recitation, public reading, radio and television broadcasting are strictly
reserved. Permission for any use of the play must be obtained in writing
from Georges Borchardt, Literary Agent, 100 West 55th Street, New York
19, N.Y.

SEQUENCE II

Look, like this. [*Stupefying young man: what is he doing?
Armed with a ballpoint pen, George is piercing holes in
the largest of the colored panels. Each hole becomes a
luminous point, because the chandelier in the smaller salon
in the back is lighted. Laurette makes a shocked gesture.*]

SIMON. Hey! George! . . . Oh . . . Oh . . . [*George goes on
piercing.*] George, for goodness' sake! [*George pierces more
energetically.*] Really, George . . . [*Simon, deciding to
laugh; interested in spite of himself.*] . . . Ah . . . Ah!
————You're unique! . . . Tell me: how many characters
are there in your dream?

GEORGE [*stops piercing. He turns toward the audience, with
arms outstretched*]. —And they were all around me, those
little lights, on the hills. They were following the slopes of the
hills; storeyed hills, probably.

LAURETTE [*not altogether conciliatory*]. I'll put etchings over
the holes.

GEORGE [*coming back toward the audience, arms wide apart*].
It was extraordinary. There was more, an aimless flight along
the bank of a river, in a city, a city with columns and marble
horses. . . .

I had taken refuge in some sort of marble tomb. A brightly
lighted tomb—neon-lighted, to be exact. I had taken refuge
there; in the marble basement—like—a kind of—café basement. The lavatory—Yes, all right—No! no, don't laugh!
—no-no-no. I might have been in the toilet, that's quite
possible, but it was really more like the bottom of a well in
which I would have liked to lose myself like a maddened
wounded beast————a hiding place and, at the same time, a
kind of monument . . . vertical, narrow and high, all right,
okay, like a toilet.

SIMON [*deeply concerned*]. Yes. . . .

LAURETTE [*laughing, her neck flexible, to Simon*]. Ah ha. . . . Funny, isn't it? Awfully funny. . . .

SIMON. Hm, yeah, sure. —But don't go, Mr. Manassé. Please. . . .

MR. MANASSÉ. It's that . . . suddenly I don't feel so good. . . .

SIMON. No. Wait a moment. [*Confidentially to Manassé.*] Don't rush him. [*He whispers in his ear, indicating George with his chin. To George.*] —Yes. Pretty banal, old man. We'll all go . . . in our dreams we all go to the end of the world. . . . Really, you surprise me, George. —Sit down.

GEORGE [*remains standing*]. No, not at all. You don't understand. It's because I'm expressing myself badly.

SIMON. Illuminations, right? Stars in the night, that's nothing extraordinary. ——Besides, I. . . . /

GEORGE. [*Slow, wide gestures, to indicate the "hills."*] But they're not stars! It's . . . it was the *tide* of houses; it was —overwhelmingly—the human presence /

SIMON [*very grave. Possible solution of the problem*]. Phosphorescent?

GEORGE. No, no, not at all.

LAURETTE [*not so dumb as all that*]. Oh, but. I understand what he means: all those little houses on the hills, in the night.

GEORGE. Yes, that's it.

SIMON. Okay. All right. Fine. Next you'll be running, galloping along a river in the middle of the night. Fine. Some sort of complex. Should be looked into. ——Yes. Yes! It's very true what I'm saying: you're so obsessed with escaping that you're running where? Very prosaically—: into the toilet. . . . What a situation. . . .

GEORGE. But listen. . . .

SIMON [*thinking rather hard, in contrast to what he is saying*]. Yeah . . . Anything is possible . . . of course. Anything can be done—masterpieces, based on anything, on any subject——Please, Mr. Manassé—just another minute—obviously. . . . But, no. No, it's of no interest to me. [*He sits down, crosses his legs and lights a cigarette.*]

GEORGE [*provoked*]. But how can you / ! —But I'm telling you this dream—of course I'm telling it to interest you, but mainly because it is an interesting dream and not . . . / I don't have the slightest / desire to show off. . . . / I'm telling it because I'm moved. . . . Laurette. . . .

LAURETTE. Yes. Yes, of course. Very pretty: those lights are very pretty. . . .

SIMON. Is there at least some adventure in your story, in your dream, since it is a dream?

GEORGE. But that's all it is, one long marvelous adventure!

SIMON. But . . . uh. . . . How does it play for sound?

GEORGE. Listen to me . . . for once . . . you might. . . .

(SEQUENCE III: Mr. Manassé gets up to go. Simon sees him to the front door.)

SEQUENCE IV

. . . .

GEORGE [*with great tenderness*]. Tell me how you are, Laurette: how are you *really*?
[*He sits down next to her on the couch.*]

LAURETTE. Same as ever . . .

GEORGE. You're not happy then. Not the least little bit happy?

LAURETTE. [*Pause. Struggling with her unhappiness.*] . . . Listen. He slapped me again after lunch. . . .

GEORGE. Oh! ——That! . . . And just after eating? . . . What had you done?

LAURETTE. [*a few tears.*] Nothing. Absolutely nothing . . .

GEORGE [*coaxing; with great tenderness*].You're telling me the truth? Is that really true, Laurette?

LAURETTE. Yes . . . Nothing at all, I told you. Nothing . . .

GEORGE. But is it really true that he dared, that he really. . . . that he . . .

LAURETTE. There, look, right there. . . . [*She shows her cheek*.]

GEORGE. Oh!! . . . My poor child. Oh . . . oh yes . . . there . . .

LAURETTE. If that were all, it wouldn't be so bad. . . .

GEORGE. Still . . .

LAURETTE. . . . but he's unfaithful! . . .

GEORGE [*Surprise and passionate curiosity*.] Oh? . . . Oh, he's unfaithful?

LAURETTE. . . . Unless that, too, doesn't matter any more. . . . unless the worst is in these hours, all day long. . . . If you knew, George, if you knew . . .

GEORGE [*passionately*]. Oh . . . how stupid of me—to have come to you, to you, to tell you my dream. [*He puts his arm around her shoulders*.]

LAURETTE. No, George, no, no.

GEORGE. If you knew how much I want to kiss you . . .

LAURETTE [*sadly*]. . . . No. [*She puts her hand on his cheek, a gesture of ostentatious friendship*.]

GEORGE [*deeply involved*]. Listen to me, Laurette. . . . Don't cry—we'll be very embarrassed, both of us, because it's going to show. [*He suddenly tries to kiss her on the mouth*.]

LAURETTE [*struggling, turning her head away*]. No! . . . George! ——George . . . ! Not like this, not like this. [*She pushes him away, making no bones about it*.]

GEORGE [*gives up, but holds on to her hand*]. Oh but—that was tenderness . . . ——My little Laurette, do you trust me?

LAURETTE [*shoulder to shoulder*]. Ye-s . . . Yes . . . .

SEQUENCE V. *Simon's noisy return.*

[*George gets up.*]

SIMON [*satisfied; full of health*]. Well now! How are we getting
along in this department? —Eh? ——Listen. [*He moves his
tongue around inside his mouth.*] Listen carefully . . .——
[*Compunction.*] I've been thinking. [*He picks a tooth.*]

One might . . . Of course one might; yes; one might be
able to do something with your dream,

Why not? ——I don't know what you're going to tell us,
but *I* have an idea now. [*He lights a cigarette.*]

GEORGE [*twisting his hands*]. You see, it may be purely suggestive, but the emotion——Yes, what I felt was so exceptional . . .

SIMON. Okay, kid. Tell me all. Tell us.

LAURETTE [*happily*]. Simon called you kid, George. That's a
good sign. Cheer up.

GEORGE. It seemed to me so . . . so exceptional/

SIMON [*laughing*]. But I'm fond of our Georgie-boy. It's when
I call him Mr. that I'm dreaming a little . . . me, too!
Huh! Huh! Go ahead, kid, tell us, go ahead. [*Change of tone.*]
Laurette, the tea!

LAURETTE [*nicely*]. Oh, yes, of course. [*She goes out.*]

GEORGE [*obstinate*]. But what I wanted to say: this emotion
—so exceptional—it's still there, right now . . . and I
thought I should—I felt the need/

SIMON. Sure, sure. Go ahead. Yes, now—right away, while it's
still hot. Sit down, kid. [*George sits down.*] That's it. Sit back
a little further. Lean back. Relax. ——Take it easy./ Would
you like some cookies? [*Simon sits down too.*]

GEORGE. No, no.

SIMON. Laurette! George wants some cookies.

LAURETTE [*from the kitchen*]. Oh! I almost scalded myself. . . . . . !

SIMON. What's wrong?

LAURETTE. I spilled everything . . .

SIMON. You're joking?——You're doing it on purpose?

LAURETTE. No.

SIMON. Oh all right, all right. Come back. / [*To George.*] Go ahead, talk, hurry up.

[*Laurette appears and sits down on the edge of the couch.*]

GEORGE. But it's. . . . It's difficult.

SIMON. Excuse me for interrupting. —Did Pigonard come, Laurette?

LAURETTE. [*She gets up and goes toward Simon.*] Yes. He left a manuscript for you.

SIMON. Okay. [*To George.*] Now then, go ahead. —Yes, go ahead: fast. I'll interrupt you if it doesn't go / [*To Laurette.*] You saw your mother?

GEORGE [*beginning his narration*]. Listen . . . : I was/

SIMON. Wait, wait. [*To Laurette.*] You saw your mother? She's not coming tomorrow? . . . So much the better! Did you /

GEORGE [*getting up*]. I was standing I don't know where, not before the landscape but: inside the landscape.

SIMON. Wait, wait, wait; one second. [*To Laurette.*] You went to the studio?

LAURETTE. Yes, yes.

SIMON [*to Laurette*]. So? Was Marsan there?

GEORGE. No but, if you think . . .

LAURETTE [*to Simon*]. Yes, he was there—but the third part has to be done over. I'll have to go back with your recordings and the new reels: the thunderstorm reels.

SIMON. When?

LAURETTE. Soon. What time is it? ——In a few moments. [*She looks at her watch.*]

GEORGE. But I'm probably disturbing you. Would you like me to go?

SIMON. No, no, I don't want you to go . . . —Ah, that's annoying, how annoying. [*Directly to George.*] Huh? Now that you've punched all those holes you might as well make use of the setting.

GEORGE. . . . Were you very fond of them, Laurette, of these decorative panels? They're not worth anything. . . .

LAURETTE [*a little forced*]. Yes, I was fond of them. You're quite right. I was rather fond of them—but it doesn't matter.

SIMON [*very energetic. Completely unexpected vocal aggression.*] Go ahead, go ahead, go ahead, go ahead! [*Abruptly, while getting up.*] You're running along the river bank as fast as you can. You cross a midway: stands; toy airplanes. Records; wheels of fortune—you are a prisoner in the crowd; you fall; you get up again; you run faster, you cross an empty square——It's Sunday. An empty square. Everything is dead, the streets are deserted, a café is open——You go down into the basement, into the toilet—and then what happens?

GEORGE [*getting up*]. Oh but /

SIMON. [*Wide gestures.*] Wait, wait. I'll start all over: "He is running. He is panting [*In a kind of declamatory frenzy*]: There is the river; a barge, sirens; no, no, it's Sunday . . . All right, it's not Sunday. . . . No, it better be Sunday— But the river, what can we do with the river———Ah!! He arrives at the fair. . . . That's ex-cel-lent.

Barrel organs, records, shooting—bang-bang, bang-bang —attention . . . watch it now . . . it's coming, there—I have it! bang-bang-bang-bang, the shooting calls up something terrible in him. He sweats, he chokes with anguish. We need some sort of inner monologue—see Faulkner /

GEORGE [*walking behind Simon*]. But Simon, please Simon!

SIMON. Shut up, kid. [*Trance.*] . . . "I have been running for thirty minutes, it's over, a curtain of sweat salts my mouth— She is dead—dead, dead, dead! It had to be, fate had it coming, I hear moaning and it's my own voice"—Noises. A chorus with a bell solo in the background.

LAURETTE [*in a whisper*]. Don't interrupt him, George. Don't interrupt.

SIMON [*in the same declamatory tone*]. Shut up, Laurette—Or —I'll spank—you! [*Going right on.*] "And here I am at a fair"—music; very good! "All these joyous people, everybody joyous, I slip into the crowd around the shooting gallery, the girl next to me is cu-u-ute, but it's all over for me, you can look at me, beautiful, it's over, it's all over, look at me sweating, I look deep into your eyes, you beautiful twenty-year-old girl, I look deep into your eyes and you see right through me /"

GEORGE [*standing, narrow silhouette*]. It's not like that, but it could be good—It's absolutely wrong but it could be a little like that—Did she guess everything?

SIMON [*about face*]. Who?

GEORGE. The girl.

SIMON [*continuing, chewing each word*]. "You have seen my sweat and you have seen my anguish, my hands red with blood if I had not washed them /"

GEORGE. But not at all! No, no /

SIMON [*even more declamatory*]. "I am the fu-gi-tive. I have bitten into the flesh. I flee from this noise, I flee from joy, I am running through deserted streets /

GEORGE. No! No!

SIMON. YES! YES! —: Deserted streets, on a Sunday: that's beautiful: Laforgue! A piano, a little girl at the window, do-mi-sol! The fugitive crosses this zone of happiness, of lost happiness—That's how society wanted it. "I'm a good-for-nothing!"

GEORGE. I'm not saying that!

LAURETTE. George!

SIMON. I am a murderer!

GEORGE. No!

SIMON [*tentative*]. A thief.

GEORGE. No!!

SIMON [*suggesting*]. A rapist.

GEORGE. Not that either!!

SIMON [*peremptory, reaffirming*]. A rapist!

GEORGE. You're forcing me, yes, you're forcing me.

SIMON. Well-what-seems-to-be-the matter? . . .

SEQUENCE VI

GEORGE [*contorted*]. But you want just the opposite from me. You're at the opposite pole.

SIMON [*seriously*]. At the pole? If I understood correctly, you are hiding in the basement, in a certain small enclosure?

GEORGE [*whining*]. No, no—Well, yes, but that's not where we are, we're not anywhere near there. Before, before, when I left [*lovingly, with open arms.*]—or rather when I *was walking* toward that sea of small twinkling lights—All those lights saying the word "presence" . . .
[*Laurette gets up to go to the kitchen.*]

SIMON. Yes, yes . . . . NO! Sit down, Laurette. Never—mind—the—tea. Too late. [*To George.*] Yes, well, and then what?

GEORGE. . . . . and after I opened my arms to this nocturnal landscape all pierced with /

SIMON. Yes, yes: those lights. And then what?

GEORGE. Well, then I found myself before the city.

SIMON. Ah!

GEORGE. A deserted city . . .

SIMON [*disconsolate, and picking at his tooth*]. Oh dear, oh dear . . .

GEORGE [*Quickly*]. No-no please. Please Simon, let me go on. ——absolutely deserted . . . [*Slowly again.*] The river was

flowing, dark, but animated by small elongated reflections
—and the river banks, or rather: its flanks, its flanks which
plunged, its flanks were so very wide—immense—marble
beaches—over which hovered, not terror, but a sort of grave
beauty . . .

SIMON. . . . Yeah . . .

[*Simon sits down.*]

GEORGE. . . . And I was walking on top of these banks. The
houses are mute, snuffed out.

SIMON. But the lights?

GEORGE. I don't know. The houses have porticos and they are
as high as temples, just like temples with cornices, columns,
and there are titles, gilded letters /

SIMON. [*Brutal distress.*] But they're banks!

GEORGE. . . . Yes! Precisely—[*Very delicately*]: Oh, you
follow me so well . . . —The emerging moon illuminates
the silhouettes of sculptured animals. Sculptured animals,
sometimes rearing . . .

But I'm wrong. —Why did I destroy the preceding moment? —Why describe facts when they hardly exist, when
everything is important, when everything is precious——
since everything, in my dream, is truth, useful truth.

[*Simon makes gestures to Laurette which she does not understand. She looks at Simon expectantly, with an amused,
ironical expression.*]

GEORGE [*who has noticed*]. . . . Don't laugh, Laurette . . .
[*Continuing almost painfully*] Why did I not insist upon my
silhouette which appeared facing the distant city . . .

LAURETTE [*blundering out of mischievousness*]. Always persecuted, poor George . . .

GEORGE. Me? Why?

[*Laurette under Simon's stern look. He is exasperated.*]

LAURETTE [*trying to justify herself*]. . . . He said I was laughing.

SIMON [*in an outburst*]. Don't upset him, please! Don't be ridiculous! Can't you see that it has to come out—afterwards we'll see . . . ! Since I stayed, at least let it be of some use!

LAURETTE [*changed, rearranging her hair*]. But you've got plenty of time.

SIMON. Go ahead, George. Go ahead. ——What? What did you say, Laurette?

LAURETTE. Nothing.

SIMON. Yes, you did!

LAURETTE. ——I said you had plenty of time.
   [*A storm in the air.*]

SIMON. How could I? ——since I was in a hurry.

LAURETTE [*cutting*]. You needn't be in a hurry. —It's only a quarter to six. —Tuesdays and Fridays you leave at six o'clock. Your Tuesday evening engagement.

SIMON. Oh!!!

LAURETTE [*very stiff, triumphant*]. Proceed, George, proceed.

GEORGE. I opened my arms, overcome with an emotion I could not explain. [*He strikes the pose, arms upraised and apart.*]

LAURETTE [*Outburst. Tears. Head down on her chest.*] Bastard!!!——!——!
   [*Sobs. Laurette buries her face in her elbow.*]

SIMON [*violently; furious and worried to George*]. Never mind! —She doesn't give a damn about my broadcasts. She doesn't give a damn about my position! Go ahead!

GEORGE [*whining*]. Oh really, oh . . . Where was I? [*He strikes his pose again; badly.*] I'm getting completely confused. . . . Yes . . . : I was hoping to describe it better . . . [*Directly to Simon. Change of tone. Speaking of Laurette.*] She is crying . . . Primordial instant of valleys, this very first moment of the pierced night / [*Same action.*] She is crying . . . / copiously through tiny blinking /

SIMON [*soaring, falling back into sitting position. Twitching about on his chair.*] Oh!! Listen: Enough lights! I've had enough lights, finally. . . . I'm going crazy! [*He wipes his forehead.*]

GEORGE [*very nice*]. . . . She isn't crying any more . . .

LAURETTE [*wet with grief, but suave out of spite*]. Go on, George. I love your lights.

GEORGE [*"very soft."*] No, Simon. You must understand. Laurette is right: you must love the lights.

SIMON [*fanning himself, very red in the face*]. Enough. ENOUGH! ——Ah . . .

GEORGE. The lights are the initial element that places everything under the sign of a general *fascination* and effusion. . . . You understand? —Otherwise I'd rather not go on . . .

SIMON. Oh!!———Go ahead, go ahead . . .

SEQUENCE VII

GEORGE [*remembering everything. With emotion*]. But how better to present this city which offers itself from a distance with all its little lights signaling . . . I said: lights—than to try to be this distant city myself . . .

[*Radiant.*] *I* the city, like this, immensely [*Arms swinging.*] with this generous movement of little valleys . . .

SIMON [*worried*]. Yes . . . yes, yes.

GEORGE [*meticulous, scrupulous*]. But how, if I am the city, how can I at the same time be my own silhouette? Since I am the one who goes toward this landscape, toward this city. Yes, to be myself the actor of what I have lived also remains . . . primordial.

SIMON. . . . . . .

GEORGE [*undecided and exquisite*]. And yet I should like to be this unknown landscape. . . . But I should also like to be those lights. . . . But how?

[*Capriciously.*] I must choose. Listen, I was right, it's better to let the perforations play the role of the distant city.

SIMON [*under pressure*]. What?

GEORGE [*in front of the perforated panels, seizing a ballpoint pen*]. There. Yes. That was fine [*Very rapidly he punches holes in the panels. All holes become luminous points*], but too general.

We must have more holes.

[*George punches holes.*]

SIMON [*getting up, decisive*]. Very good. Very, very good. Let's make holes, holes!

[*Both men punch holes as fast as they can.*]

LAURETTE. No please! Simon! George!

SIMON [*full action*]. Never mind. Never mind. He wants holes and he shall have them! [*Many small luminous points.*] It's "primordial"! [*To George.*] Go ahead. Since you started, you may as well continue.

GEORGE [*contemplative*]. Lovely, isn't it?

SIMON [*false joviality after an effort*]. Lovely, a lovely decoration. Very suggestive. There. [*Affected and bitter.*] Another one up here, what do you think?

GEORGE [*"on a point."*] Not too far to the right.

SIMON. Laurette, where are you going?

LAURETTE [*stiffly*]. You don't require my presence, I hope?

SIMON. Stay here.

LAURETTE. Oh, let me go—I can't let the gas burn for nothing!

[*The two men against the background of luminous points.*]

GEORGE. Hurry back, Laurette, you'll be very, very useful. You'll be the river.

SIMON [*"good-natured" and furious. To Laurette.*] Stay here! You'll be the river.

GEORGE. Yes, languidly stretched out on the couch, your head on your elbow. The classical pose, as it were.

SIMON. That's it.

GEORGE [*director of operations*]. The couch must be pulled
out.

[*Simon takes off his jacket.*]

GEORGE [*steps back to judge*]. These lights *are* very suggestive,
aren't they . . . ! But we no longer know exactly . . .

SIMON. Huh?

GEORGE. . . . They are the lights. . . [*greedily*] but soon
they'll become the stars filling the city sky.

SIMON [*throwing himself into the job*]. C'mon. Help me pull
out the couch. —That's it, the houses will be the stars! Push!

[*Laurette returns.*]

GEORGE. Lie down, Laurette.

SIMON. He's telling you to get on the couch. ——[*Laurette sits
down on the edge of the couch.*] But wait, wait. [*Searching
the table with his eyes.*]   Where is the typewriter ribbon?

LAURETTE. What for? You want to write? You want to type?

GEORGE. What? But . . .

SIMON [*sitting down before the typewriter*]. No, no, no, no,
no, don't get nervous. [*Laurette gives the ribbon to Simon.*]
Don't pay any attention to me—stay in your dream. [*Ma-
nipulating the ribbon.*] There, let's see—No, go ahead,
talk, I'm listening . . . [*Quickly to Laurette*]: Go lie
down—on the couch. . . .

SEQUENCE VIII

. . . You're in the country, at night and you—[*He starts
typing*] at night /

GEORGE. But wait /

SIMON [*typing*]. At night. It is not yet late enough—for—the
hou—ses to have closed their shutters—Uh . . . everything blinks—and the commuters—traveling to the suburbs
—of Paris—the inhabitants of the suburbs—are familiar
with this effect /

GEORGE. But /

SIMON. [*Loud*]. at least those who—live—in the valleys. Approaching on—an open road at—nine o'clock in the evening, one sees—the lighted suburbs. Next?

GEORGE. No—no. That's not it . . . !

SIMON. What do you mean: that's not it!

GEORGE [*terribly impeded, "capricious"*]. First of all, Laurette isn't a good river . . . and then you . . . Oh Laurette, I'd rather have just the couch . . . without you . . .

SIMON [*to Laurette, earnestly, his hands suspended above the keyboard.*] Get up.

[*Laurette gets off the couch.*]

GEORGE. The couch is the river. —[*To Laurette.*] You'll play the part of a young girl later . . . —[*To himself.*] I stand before the river . . . [*Standing, not far from Simon's writing table, that is in the center of the stage. George closes his eyes and extends his arms slightly.*]

SIMON [*gravely*]. Cross it . . . [*He types.*]

GEORGE. . . . Look out /

SIMON [*interrupting himself*]. You're jumping in? You're swimming?

GEORGE. No, no. I'm walking on the bridge.

SIMON [*slow, hearty comment*]. You're right. ——[*And he types.*]

GEORGE. The streets are deserted; the lamps are lighted. I am at the other end of the bridge . . .

SIMON [*types fast and speaks slowly*]. Wait . . . Don't run so fast, wait for me . . .

GEORGE [*very happy, his eyes shining*]. Ah, but—I'm not running, I advance, as though I were being carried . . .

SIMON. Fine; wait; I have to cross out. There . . . : "Gerard walks on the bridge."

GEORGE [*terribly disturbed*]. What do you mean: Gerard?!

SIMON. Shut up! [*Typing.*] Slapping water—noise of foot steps—Shut up.

"He takes long strides."

GEORGE [*again wrapped up in his narration. Helpfully*]. No. ——I'm just walking.

SIMON [*same action*]. Okay. —"Gerard—walks—with slow— steps."

GEORGE. Wait, wait . . . [*Simon stops typing.*] . . . : neither fast nor slow.

SIMON. Okay—okay. [*He types.*]

GEORGE. I'm walking . . .

SIMON. "Easily."

GEORGE. Ah? I'm going too fast?

SIMON. No, no. I say you walk easily. [*Re-reading, satisfied.*] I like "easily." Easily is pretty. [*Pronounce:* Prit—ttee.]

GEORGE. Yes. . . . Well, I'm just walking . . .

SIMON. "Easily."

GEORGE. Oh I'm sorry; I'm walking easily, that's right, across the poorly lighted bridge . . . above the marble river banks —and the black water . . .

SIMON. [*re-reading aloud*]. "Gerard crosses easily, and surreptitiously above the marble embankments." [*Typing.*] Slipping water.

GEORGE. What?

SIMON. Nothing, nothing. Go ahead . . .

GEORGE [*taking a few tentative steps*]. . . . And I find myself on the inhabited bank which contrasts strongly with the one I have just left, the one which was deserted, but so beautiful——Listen, on one of the cornices there was a horse . . . ! / Against the cloudy sky a marble horse . . . ! . . .

SIMON [*hands off the keyboard, and persuasive*]. Yes, but try to understand, the marble horse, you can see it, but you can't hear it . . . [*Typing again*] So you're on the other side: Sequence Two.

GEORGE. I've crossed the bridge.

SIMON. Yes, I know.

GEORGE. I find myself before huge lighted buildings / and in their lobbies, and on the floor of these lobbies, there is a crowd. The crowd climbs the stairs, and through the glass walls you can see people climbing.

SIMON [*typing*]. "Gerard among the shopping crowd in the business district . . ."

GEORGE. Oh, what did you say? No! / Well, yes, stores, yes. . . . But that's not how they looked . . .

SIMON [*same action*]. "He slips through the crowd. People chatter around him. Hawkers shout their wares."

GEORGE [*plaintive; fragile; groping*]. The beauty was the way I said it . . . precisely because the word store did not come to mind. . . . It was more like human *beehives,* agitated, absurd and poignant. Let me say it. [*Returning to the tone of "loving" narration.*] I go into a store swarming with people /

SIMON [*typing*]. . . . "Swarming with people / Picturesque crowd / Atmosphere."

GEORGE [*satisfied and on tiptoe*]. / and I don't know how, nor why, but, but I slap a sales girl in the face. . . . Yes: I slap her. [*Sensation.*]

SIMON. Huh?

LAURETTE. Oh!

GEORGE. As hard as I can . . . —Oh—oh—I'm sorry, Laurette . . .

LAURETTE. But why?

GEORGE. . . .

SIMON [*typing, radiant, drawling*]. But that's good! That's very, very good . . . !

Trends in the Contemporary
French Novel

by HENRI PEYRE

It is doubtless fortunate that the many prophecies ventured every year by literary critics are forgotten almost as soon as are the political and economic forecasts of historians and social scientists. The latter err most often on the side of excessive optimism and paint the material future of men in Western lands in glowing hues. The former prefer to be prophets of gloom. They nod their heads mournfully at the prospect of the death of tragedy, the moribund condition of poetry, the disappearance of the essay. The death of the novel was, until 1940 or so, one of their favorite topics. These conservatives, nostalgic for the solid, earnest fiction they had read in their youth, averted their horrified gaze from the "formless" novels which an anti-Victorian age offered them. They absorbed, lock, stock and barrel, the structure of frail generalizations handed over to them by Marxism. They glibly repeated that the rise of the novel had somehow and very mysteriously been bound up with the ascent of the bourgeoisie. They concluded that, as the bourgeoisie went on collapsing (has it ever been stronger than in its victorious answer to the many challenges thrown at it since

1917? has it ever been more fertile in literary and artistic talents who, emerging from its midst, whip it ferociously, because they know its capacity for endurance?), the novel would become the fixture of outworn creeds and of a bygone era.

The French novel almost perished three or four times in the last eighty years: first during symbolism and when Anatole France and Pierre Loti were taken to be its most skilled practitioners; then when some overconscientious workmen like Paul Bourget and Romain Rolland attempted to pour ideas and social preaching into it; then when autobiographical, thin novels on adolescents imprisoned in their solipsism followed perilously on the footsteps of André Gide, Julien Green, Jean Cocteau and others; again lately when philosophers turned into novelists, advocated commitment and lavishly disserted through their Kierkegaardian characters on the human condition and on living existentially.

After every false death, however, a rebirth came. In the early nineteen fifties, the colorful flowering of the French novel of 1930–1950 (Bernanos, Céline, Giono, Malraux; then Camus, Sartre, Simone de Beauvoir) appeared to be withering into an autumnal decrepitude. The sturdy impulse once received from the new American fiction had ceased to spur French writers to emulation of transatlantic violence. Byzantine disquisitions on form in the novel and time in the novel, on symbolic structure and on the language of the novelist were paralyzing the fiction writers in a land where creators are perilously close to critics or where a critic lurks in the brain cells of every would-be imaginative talent. Joyce—following upon Mallarmé's meditations on *the* great work that was to supplant all other books and provide, through speculations on language and silence, the total orphic explanation of the world—was regarded as the grave digger of Western fiction.

The French, happily, are a fickle nation. Their usable past is so broad that they periodically decide to disregard most of it and to turn away from the impressive giants of yesterday to the defunct giants of an even earlier age, less likely to overshadow them. They treat these ancestors with insolent and refreshing familiarity. They redo Laclos, Rétif, Sade, Stendhal, and Benjamin Constant—with a difference. The novel, that phoenix among literary kinds, overprompt to return to dust, vigorously emerges from its heap of ashes. Critics and journalists hail "the new novel" of the new France. A Gaullist era in literature is ushered in, for which the grave sovereign is hardly more responsible than Queen Victoria was for Emily Brontë or Thackeray or Meredith. Publicity is promptly organized or encouraged. Foreign publishers order translations. English-speaking schoolboys will soon lay aside their favorite textbook, *L'Etranger*, and bid farewell to their nonvocal French hero, Meursault the involuntary murderer, for school editions of *La Jalousie* or *La Modification*. School girls will learn all about the French woman from *Le Repos du Guerrier* and *Aimez-vous Brahms*.

The new novelists of France are in truth a motley crowd, at least as varied as are the young and not-so-young men in anger in Britain or the crop of post-World War II American novelists ranging from Saul Bellow and Norman Mailer to William Styron and the author of *The Catcher in the Rye*. Being French, however, they had to formulate, hence to invent, a body of doctrinal views to clarify their own aims and to impress the philosophical reviewers. And, although they do not seem, like the Madrid writers, to be the habitués of a particular "tertulia" or to have yet selected their favorite café, they are labeled by the public as a school. Like all "schools," they would be more likely to agree on their grounds for disagreeing with their predecessors than on any common aims. The leftist Catholic *Esprit,* one of the most thoughtful monthlies in Europe at the present time and the freest from any constricting allegiance to any cause, devoted a substantial number, in July-August 1958, to the *"nouveau roman."* Ten of these younger novelists, ranging in age from twenty-five to fifty-five (Beckett) and fifty-seven (Nathalie Sarraute), were selected by the contributors to *Esprit* as the most significant: Samuel Beckett, Michel Butor, Jean Cayrol, Marguerite Duras, Jean Lagrolet, Robert Pinget, Alain Robbe-Grillet, Nathalie Sarraute, Claude Simon, Kateb Yacine. Another dozen might easily be added to that list: among the women, Françoise des Ligneris, Noelle Loriot, Christiane Rochefort and Françoise Mallet-Joris, already author of four novels though not yet thirty years old; among the men, if Roger Nimier, Roger Vailland, Romain Gary, Félicien Marceau, the revelation of the years immediately following World War II, are relegated to the antechamber of the Academy, the conspicuous names are those of André Gorz—lavishly praised by Sartre—Jacques Howlett, Bernard Pingaud, Bertrand Poirot-Delpech, Philippe Sollers and the author of a new epic novel of the persecuted Jewish race, Schwarz-Bart.

It is naturally preposterous to attempt a generalization on the trends discernible in so many novelists which would fit all of them: individualism is not dead, even in a France which is supposed to show signs of Americanization and to accept austerity meekly if cheerlessly. Literary trends are ultimately imposed by the greatness of isolated individuals who happen to have broken through a previously blind alley and to have led many followers behind the trail they blazed. Proust and Malraux are now seen, in retrospect, as having expressed the trends, Proust of the 'twenties, Malraux of the 'thirties. Will any of the new novelists grow into an author of similar stature? The thing is by no means impossible. To our contemporary eyes, Michel Butor, perhaps Claude Simon and Claude Ollier, less probably Alain Robbe-Grillet and Nathalie Sarraute may develop into novelists of real greatness. But they write for their times and we, their immediate contemporaries, may naïvely state what we see in them as of today.

First the tradition of the *récit* is maintained by the younger writers: if they rebel against Flaubert and even more against Balzac, they revere Benjamin Constant and apparently Raymond Radiguet's classical restraint and naïve cynicism. Stendhal is the idol which knows no iconoclast. Communist writers, like Roger Vaillard and Claude Roy, try to borrow his tone; Jean Giono labors to turn out adroit but almost embarrassing pastiches of *La Chartreuse de Parme;* rightist critics continue, long after Paul Bourget, Jacques Boulenger, and Maurice Bardèche, to be Stendhal's devotees. Such a cult makes the modern French novel too self-conscious and freezes its imaginative thrusts. Stendhal's irony and shy self-defense against his reader acted as a beneficent antidote against his romantic leanings: there is not much romantic exuberance to be tamed in our recent authors of *récits* and their sobriety often seems achieved with perilous ease. Of all masters of fiction, Stendhal may well be the most oppressive when his imitators steal only his outward mannerisms.

But sophisticated readers, who are repelled by the avalanche of wordy vitality which the American novel often rolls down upon them, turn with relief to several of the ingenious, tight-lipped and open-eyed short works of fiction in which the French excel. The best in the output of the last few years are: *L'Amour n'est qu'un plaisir* by Jean d'Ormesson; *Le Grand Dadais* (*Fool's Paradise* in the American translation published in 1959) by the new drama critic of *Le Monde,* Bertrand Poirot-Delpech; and *Moderato Cantabile* by Marguerite Duras. They are masterfully written, with that swift, racing, lucid pace of the eighteenth-century story tellers, rushing to their feminine conquests and eventually to the scaffold. *Le Grand Dadais* is a confessional tale in the first person, by a young man who appears to be a clumsy and innocent fool, but who in fact cherishes much cynical ambition behind his mask. He caused the death of another man, was indicted for murder, faced the judges with some insolence and was imprisoned for five years.

The age-old theme of a prisoner, to which the fate of Europe, turned into a huge prison camp during the war years, lent new and tragic significance, haunts several of the writers of today. Bernard Pingaud's *Le Prisonnier,* inspired by a painting by Georges de la Tour, gravely but coldly written, is another one of these indirect protests of man, "the innocent convict," against the prison of his condition.

Moderato Cantabile is a deftly wrought utilization of musical structure by an expert woman novelist. The words allude to the piano lessons taken, listlessly and rebelliously, by a child whom his mother fails to understand. His mother is strangely fascinated by a scene to which she is a witness: a man kills a young woman, for love, and kisses her dead body passionately. She identifies herself with the woman thus loved to the point of death and beyond it, while a factory worker whom she meets at a café appears to her, in spite of the class barrier between them, as he who might also have "killed the thing he loved." Nothing happens; an inner drama is merely hinted, with a superb economy of means.

Such self-control verges perilously on the sort of intellectual tyranny exercised by the novelist over his characters which has always been the weakness of French fiction. John Galsworthy, who used to admire that artistic discipline in Flaubert and Maupassant, contrasted it with the tendency of the English novel "to go to bed drunk." The American novel has, since Galsworthy's time, replaced the English one as the garrulous and torrential drunkard. The French have become weary of these characters who are led on a leash by their creator and never seem to waylay him where he had not premeditated to venture. Strict sparseness of language and diminution of little facts, in appearance insignificant, may also harm credibility and render the author's watchful presence obtrusive. It it easy to be amused by some of the most highly praised novels of the last season (1958–59), but the intellect and our sense of de-

TRENDS IN CONTEMPORARY FRENCH NOVEL

light in irony alone are concerned: our imagination and our feelings, after the brief intellectual or erotic titillation, remain cold.

Christiane Rochefort's *Le Repos du Guerrier,* translated as *Warrior's Rest,* sold generously, entertained widely and shocked no less violently, for it stands as far as can be from the "*roman de jeune fille*" which once was intended to preserve the virtue of the French woman up to the wedding-night revelation. A man, rescued from suicide by a girl of the French middle class, is selected by that young lady as the male who might have been a hero of the Kinsey report: he drinks as much as he makes love, and with the same zestful nonchalance. He beats his saviour lady with vigorous conviction; these scenes of correction of the female by the male must have won many feminine readers to that best seller, crowned with the Prix de la Nouvelle Vague. As some of them confessed in a subsequent questionnaire on women's aspirations, if the woman does not exactly wish to be beaten, she likes to be reassured that her male companion would at least be up to administering a few vigorous blows if he had to. In the end, after many a melancholy orgy, the woman brings her warrior to rest from whisky and probably from sex—through marriage. Then, naturally, they can be unhappy ever after in exemplary fashion. The tale is slight, though not devoid of social significance for those who wish to explore the strange forms assumed by feminine sexuality in our time; but it is told with winning naturalness.

The same could not be said of another best seller of the season, *Zazie dans le métro,* by Raymond Queneau. Like Wordsworth in his famous preface, the author, a student of language, and of Joyce, and an encyclopedist who seeks relief from his labors in prolonged flirtations with the comic muse, "brings his language near to the language of men." He waves the flag against the very notion of literature and rebels against the one convention which in the past remained sacrosanct to all revolutionaries: respect for language. But the characters are all wooden puppets, their manipulation of words is pedantic and heavy-handed and the teenager, Zazie, an insufferable and vulgar little girl, whose company would in real life prove even more tedious than Lolita's, seems to have been drawn by its ironical creator as a discouragement to the present strenuous efforts of the French at increasing their population. Many a discovery remains to be made in what Freud termed "the polymorphous perverseness" of childhood.

A more robust reaction against the traditional, brief, self-conscious, hyper-intelligent French *récit* appears in several attempts at rejuvenating the picaresque novel. Giono led the way after World War II, when his experience in a French prison cured him of preaching an idyllic life in harmony with nature and in sympathy with animals and drove him to galloping adventures across the plains and mountains of southern France and northern Italy. Louis Aragon, that underestimated Picasso of literature, a chameleon poet as Keats might have termed him and a plastic fictional talent, a master of metamorphoses yet never a posturing clown, delighted French readers in 1958 with *La Semaine Sainte*. The book is a dashing historical epic on the hundred days which preceded Napoleon's fall at Waterloo, colorful, tender, less rambling and less didactic than some picaresque novels which insist upon turning years of adventure into Goethean "*Lehrjahre*," nostalgic for the warlike glamor of the Empire as only a Communist can be. Roger Nimier, who made a startling début "*à la hussarde*" into postwar fiction and should have become one of the masters of the new French picaresque, has not yet fulfilled his promise. The analysis of love often waylays those impetuous young French conquerors into foolishly endeavoring to know women while they love them, and therefore into building up a structure of psychological labyrinthine staircases in order to pursue their baffling mistresses up and down every landing.

The most determined champion of the new picaresque has been, in the last fifteen years, Romain Gary. As early as 1946, that Russian-French diplomat, Gaullist airman, admirer of Malraux and of Stendhal, had challenged the existentialists by proclaiming: "The modern novel will be picaresque or it will not exist. Picaresque, in the sense of a fresco with a welter of adventures, of movement and of swarming characters. And of optimism, also." The author of *The Roots of Heaven* cannot help being a moralist and to hide many a message of gloom, yet of good will also, in the trunky and spacious legs of his elephants. But, with many a flaw in style and some off-handed contempt for structure, his work carried the reader along in its tempestuous sweep. The British tenants of the picaresque today, John Wain, Kingsley Amis, Angus Wilson, seem more bitter, more farcically satirical, more tightly and intellectually in rebellion against the conventions of social classes than their more generously Rabelaisian French counterparts.

The label of "*le nouveau roman*" has lately been appropriated by a particular group of novelists, far more earnest than the picaresque, the ironical and the salacious ones who maintain, in the midst of a world reveling in the absurd and proud of its sedulously cultivated anguish, the Frenchman's right to smile at what he cherishes most: women, sentiment, the illogic of life, and himself. Nathalie Sarraute and Alain Robbe-Grillet take us with pontifical gravity over the threshold of "*l'ère du soupçon*." They hold infinity, no longer in the palm of their hand, but within the crawling centipede which characters in *La Jalousie* crush repeatedly, in reality or in their nightmares, on a wall, or in the tropisms set in motion in some neurotic old lady by the imperfection of a lock applied upon an oaken door. The humor of Proust and of Sartre, the great masters of comedy, has been expelled from their Jansenist stories. So has any pampering to that vulgar expectation of naïve readers: "What is going to happen?" Their novel, like Joyce's, like Kafka's, like Gide's *Counterfeiters*, is, as it is now termed, an anti-novel. The most authentic predecessors of these doctrinaire new novelists are, even more directly, Sartre in *La Nausée* and Camus in *L'Etranger,* the two novels of the years 1935–45 that have exercised the most vivid fascination and have brought forth the most fecund progeny. But with the latest generation, absurdity is no longer encountered in the trappings of the middle class in their provincial Sunday best or in the luxuriance of a slimy root sprawling in the damp soil, in the alienation from society of an elementary hero speaking of himself as if he were "*l'étranger*." It lies in man's delusion that his existence could ever have been necessary or have mattered to objects surrounding him.

The characteristics of the "new fiction" may be defined as follows; first, away with metaphysics. *Pourquoi des Philosophes*? is the title of one of the recent pamphlets by J. Revel, an acid and impatient iconoclast bent upon deflating the silvery bubbles blown by all the teachers of philosophy who, in the 'forties, had made French fiction their sole domain. André Gorz, whose volume, *Le Traitre,* is a masterful existential psychoanalysis of the author parading as fiction, is the only overt philosopher among the younger group. Speculations on man's fate and man's responsibilities in a world of derelict mortals condemned to be free appear to most others as mere escapism into cloudy speculations, away from the sway of hard, angular objects.

Then, down with psychology, which, as Paul Valéry hinted, ever saw and seized only the exterior of what is inward. Proust had certainly added a new density to our feeling for our inner life and made Flaubert and Zola, George Eliot and Hardy appear elementary; he had dissected love, jealousy, and the intermittences of the heart into what appeared to be their ultimate component molecules. But even Proustian analysis, once it had refined the perception of the readers fit to share it, became conventional; it resorted to ready-made formulas, to lavish botanical metaphors or to cascades of harmonious adjectives. Joyce's interior monologues, once revered as the paragons of subtlety, wear off their freshness and appear crude and tricky. The impact of American fiction, impatient of hairsplitting introspection and of the Frenchman's Valeryan obsession to see himself seeing himself ("*je me voyais me voir*," as said La Jeune Parque), to watch himself eating, writing, feeling, has helped transform the French novel.

The leaders of the young movement also boast of their revolt against characters in the novel. Those characters whom Balzac and his followers believed as if they were holy entities, became congealed into types: the lover, the jealous, the upstart, the inventor, the miser, the sadist, the self-sacrificing lady. But the era of suspicion forecast by Stendhal came with a hundred years' lag. Modern man's claim is to call everything in question: liberty, justice, equality, charity, saintliness, language and the fixity of characters. Beneath those artificial categories, Nathalie Sarraute discerns formless, nascent moves, slow repetitions of our mental organs, elementary reactions of our flesh or of our nerves which never reach the stage of half-conscious elaboration in our brains. She wishes to be the Columbus of those uncharted zoological tropisms. Proust used to contend that his lenses were those of a telescope. Mme. Sarraute prefers the microscope. She strikes at the heart of the fictional phenomenon itself, by magnifying those untold unformulable tropisms which make each of us at times feel that, if only he could record them and amplify them, he would grow into a novelist. There are, few and far between, glimpses of freshness and poetry in *Le Planetarium*, but also a perilous duel with tediousness, a multiplication of minute nothings ("my son-in-law adores grated carrots . . . new, tender carrots" repeats the exasperatingly garrulous old lady) in *Le Planetarium* which may strain the much vaunted resistance to boredom of our age.

Alain Robbe-Grillet has been more explicit in his theoretical pronouncements and his novels are smoothly contrived, with at least the shell of a mystery-thriller plot, to keep the reader breathless while he skips the geometric passages. He wants to achieve nothing less than the final break between man and the universe of things, to demystify the much abused adjective "human." Let man see things "with no softness," detachedly, fully aware that things never return to him his gaze, not any more than God in His majesty. Let him cease boasting about the tragedy of being forsaken by an indifferent world and renounce the childishness of begging inanimate objects for an echo of his own sorrows. Robbe-Grillet painstakingly sizes up objects with compasses, T square and scale. He describes longitudinal, rectangular, median lines in the complexity of things, repressing all Balzacian temptation to endow objects with a visionary existence of their own, which would only be an egotistic delusion of our anthropomorphism.

The tempo of fiction is also renovated: it is that of a very slow camera, endlessly shooting at the same scene. In *Les Gommes,* not yet translated, as in *La Jalousie,* there is no continuity of an irreversible passing of time; there is no cumulative impact of a progressive narrative. Holes of darkness are skillfully provided, into which the reader may pursue one misleading track after another. Proust likewise induced us to put several fallacious interpretations on the behavior of Swann, Charlus, or Albertine, until all the masks were lifted and the truth flashed on the reader. In this new kind of cold geometric thriller, the reader remains baffled down to the end. We turn around in an eternal recurrence, living over again the same scene in anticipation, actuality and nightmarish memory. The novelist himself refrains from proposing his point of view; he wants to discover his laconic characters, exchanging few unconcerned words, at the same time as his reader does. He never analyzes them, never ponders over their psychology or moralizes on the significance of their deeds. Of the four novels published by Robbe-Grillet, *Le Voyeur* (translated as *The Voyeur*) is probably the most successful. *La Jalousie* is a trifle too tricky and *Dans le Labyrinthe* too puritanical in its fulfillment of Flaubert's dream: a novel made of and with nothing, a Mallarméean work of absence by an anti-poet.

The most authentic disciple of Robbe-Grillet is a novelist of great talent, Claude Ollier, whose *La Mise en Scène* received the newly-founded Médicis prize late in 1958. He, too, is a seer, if not a visionary seer; like the painter Monet, he is an eye, but what an eye! Every particle of the desert sand, of the barren cliffs, of the hardy tufts of dry grass, every line along a track or shade of a teapot is patiently described. The hero, Lassalle (unlike Kafka and the characters in *La Jalousie,* he is endowed with more than a mere initial) travels across the North African desert to draw the road to a mining establishment. He is beset with suspicions of his guides, gradually discovers that his predecessor was murdered and the Arab women whom he had known a little too well have been brutally punished. The theme (it cannot be called a plot) is that of a mystery story laid in the desert. But all the talent, which is rich, is lavished on the inventory of objects. Man is relegated where he belongs: he is a being without communion with things, forbidden to play the cheap game of pathetic fallacy. *"Objets inanimés, avez-vous donc une âme?"* questioned naïve Lamartine. The answer is a sharp no: human beings themselves yearn only for geometric soullessness.

Claude Simon is also fascinated by objects, their shapes, weight and color. "To know is to possess," as he claims. His vocation was that of a botanist, and in *L'Herbe,* a funereal symphony of characters who look back upon their whole lives "as they lie dying," he aimed at annihilating the story from the novel. "One does not see the story, not any more than one sees the grass growing," as he quotes from Boris Pasternak. *Le Vent* (translated as *The Wind* and courageously brought out by George Braziller) puzzled American reviewers—and understandably so. It is Faulknerian to the point of embarrassment. But the author showed that he could be at ease in a chaos and haunt us through repetitions. *L'Herbe* has more freshness and contrives striking effects of chiaroscuro in the midst of a gruesome dance of death. An old maid relives her life of devotion for creatures who did not deserve it; all is ripeness, or rather rottenness of the flesh shredded and devoured by death. There is more passion here than in *"l'école du regard,"* the school of the viewers, as the geometric land surveyors have been nicknamed; and an uncanny power over words: sentences of one hundred lines or more are child's play to that French Faulkner.

Michel Butor has been treated more generously by critics than Robbe-Grillet, Claude Ollier or Nathalie Sarraute, whom it is too easy to parody. He has not altogether renounced psychology, which reassures French academic reviewers. He, too, depicts objects minutely, but he does not dehumanize them with such fanatical relentlessness. He does not expel all symbolic connotations from his novels, and the stained-glass window of the old Bleston Cathedral, representing Abel's murder by Cain, stands for an original curse afflicting that rain-soaked city of Bleston, the forlorn Negro whom the protagonist encounters, the French man recapturing time and living it reversibly, with all its recurrences, during his dreary year in the British city of soot and fog. *L'Emploi du Temps* is, in our eyes, the richest, the most musically orchestrated and the most poetical novel of the last ten years. *La Modification,* published by Simon and Schuster as *A Change of Heart* and in London as *Second Thought* is something of a self-conscious *tour de force.* The long monologue of the traveler from Paris to Rome, observing, reminiscing, analyzing his feelings or watching them alter as he addresses himself as "*nous*," miraculously eschews boredom. The Roman mistress, loved in association with the Eternal City, but in truth loved tepidly; the nagging wife in Paris, who wins in the end in the duel of which she is unaware, come to life with mysterious vividness. The technique is impeccable yet never obtrusive. Joyce and Faulkner are never altogether absent from these sprawling monologues and the thirty- or forty-line sentences, but their example has been assimilated and naturalized. "No great novel ever came from a superficial mind," wrote Henry James to R. L. Stevenson in the last decade of the nineteenth century. Butor's mind is rich, original and subtle. He is the most authentic novelist of his generation.

Too much has doubtless been made of the phrase "the New Novel in France," and publicity rushed in too fast and too arrogantly to cash in on the band of angels whom France, weary with existentialist moralists and with eroticists, was awaiting to renovate fiction. There are many tricks in their manner, an arrogant and dogmatic self-consciousness in their doctrines, much tediousness in the practice of several of them. But this ascetic bath into purity and this "methodical experience," as Butor has called the modern novel, with lessons taken in all humility by writers from geometricians, engineers, and botanists is a salutary one. It is good that, periodically, literature in France should call everything in question, spurn the crushing weight of tradition and proceed to a systematic accumulation of new, if somewhat rough-hewn, materials. This era of suspicion is also an era of reconstruction and of faith in "a virgin and lively today."

The Asylum, a short story

by PIERRE GASCAR

Translated by URSULE MOLINARO
and VENABLE HERNDON

The asylum stood a few miles from the city, on the fringe of a working-class suburb overlooking a plain that heaved gently, like a page being turned: a page that has been read; emptied of meaning; gray with oblivion: never to be turned. A few very tall trees shaded the asylum buildings, their tollhouse isolation, which a flag over the entrance signaled to whom it might concern. In the distance the wind was pushing clouds.

Sometimes it was a summer day heavy with heat, sometimes a rainy afternoon, rarely a snow-speckled dawn, but always the same sky which ignored the seasons; it lodged madness in the slightly livid light which bathes the pictures of very old Flemish painters and gives them their lasting finish.

First there had been the interminable ride along tree-lined avenues, through low-roofed towns. Then the arrival at the asylum gates, and—after so many days of endless passing through a thousand doors—seeing them open before her would merely have provoked a mute acquiescence in Rose if, at that very moment, a man in a white smock had not bent down, with the cruel meticulousness of sanity, to remove a pebble that was blocking the door. Was the torture to begin all over again? Had they all, already, taken up their old positions?

88

"You'll see, we're going to behave very well," now said a woman, also all in white. "We'll go to the dormitory. But first we'll change our clothes."

The use of the first person plural created an exasperating climate of false complicity. At last they went out into the park. Women with untidy hairdos, all in blue dresses, daydreamed or chattered, came, went or just sat under the trees.

It was toward the end of June that Rose Schmidt, locked in a city ambulance, passed through the asylum gates. Seasons have a way of seeming endless, even though they have hardly begun. The asylum summer, with its leaves cutting almost black into the light of the sky, was as rigid, as permanent as destiny: a summer of iron lances. They slipped a hand under your arm to help you walk.

"Rose Schmidt," murmured the nurse between finely drawn lips to direct her attention while entering Rose's name in the register.

Her husband had not come with her, and one might have thought that, by registering Rose under her maiden name, the nurse was condemning her forever to his absence. Actually, as Rose found out later, the nurse was merely complying with a regulation established during the last century, which stipulated that, upon entering the asylum, all married women reverted to their maiden names.

"Rose Schmidt, born September eighteen, nineteen twenty-two," repeated the nurse who was making up a file, consulting certificates that seemed to have appeared from nowhere, "September eighteen, nineteen twenty-two . . ."

Driven by feminine curiosity she scrutinized the age of each newcomer as though she were trying to reassure herself of her own relative immunity or, at least, discover proof of some reprieve which might have been granted her; she finally emerged from her indifference.

"So we're thirty," she said, raising her eyes, "thirty."

"Miss . . ." stammered Rose.

"Brun, my name is Mrs. Brun," said the nurse with a kind of snake charmer's insistence.

Always someone to pull us toward conversation, this fluid place where we do not wish to go—always someone who has been hanging around our silence for a long, long time and who, all of a sudden, starts playing the "transparent mask."

"Miss . . ." repeated Rose with a bewildered voice, or a forgotten voice.

And her hand sketched a vague gesture against her hip. Out of reach, reality was already fleeing.

"Let's go; let's go," said another nurse who was standing in back of Rose and whom she had not seen come in.

They hurried out into the park.

. . . .

While they were dressing her in the madwomen's uniform, after the shower, Rose kept her head obstinately turned toward the barred window, toward the tops of the trees, motionless in the light of the sky. It was the only way of staying separate, of showing them that she was letting them take this sort of docility like another blouse. Allowing oneself to be dressed in blue was a way of accepting the fact that one was being stripped once more: they were dressing her in absence.

They made her lift one arm; both arms; one leg; the other leg. And every time, a back bowed down before her, but in a treacherous pose—the face of the woman, slightly raised, with a frozen smile—a back to lean on. Now both arms had to be raised again together; Rose's eyes did not leave the sky.

"Look at her, standing there like a recruit passing his physical," baa-ed a voice behind her.

They threw her a shirt and panties in harsh brown holland, a blue-and-white-checkered blouse and skirt. No stockings. She thrust her feet—ice cold from the tile floor—into a pair of slippers. She was still holding herself very straight.

"Put your head down!" yelled a nurse.

She obeyed. Impatient hands rummaged through her hair, braided it, knotted it into a bun. They gave her two dull black combs with uneven teeth. Rose let the combs drop to the floor. She was finally breaking down; she had tried too hard up to now. Her legs buckled under her; her knees and hands touched the tiles. But she did not stretch out; she guessed that then they would carry her off through more doors, and afterwards one can never be sure to find them all again, you know, one wanders forever in empty, faintly echoing halls. . . .

"Do you think she ought to be put to bed?" a woman asked, obsequiously eager. She had come up, dressed in the same blue and white as Rose. "Look, she's squatting there like a toad."

"No; but you may take her out to get some air in the court-yard," replied the nurse.

The woman bent down and grabbed Rose under the arms.

"Come on! Stand up!" she cried, already drunk with her authority.

Rose had recovered from her faintness. She stood up. The woman in blue took her hand. She was an old woman with a flat face; the skin of her cheeks glistened like the new skin of someone who has been burned, but it was yellow and deeply lined. She had a slightly jerky walk that strained hard for dignity, and this aimless excursion through corridors that all looked alike became for Rose—after the exactions, the recent scold-ings, the chaos of gestures and words—what horse trainers or men of the ring call "the cooling-off period," a slow-motion walk, almost dreamlike, but during which a kind of "stepping," blood-shot eyes still unable to see, a sobbing movement of the shoulders, betray the long disaster of violence, the unredeemed effort.

"One-two; one-two," murmured the old woman at every second step, caught in the majesty of the rite.

But the slippers were too loose for Rose's feet. She stumbled.

"Pick up your feet!" ordered the old woman.

The spell was broken. Rose hung her head, staring at her veined feet in the formless slippers, fascinated by their penitent nakedness.

They had entered a great hall, furrowed by long marble tables with benches lined up on either side. A stale odor rose from the iron sink along the wall. Women came and went, with nothing to do, living out their patience.

One of them came up. "A new one?" she asked.

"Yes," answered the old woman, "and I'm teaching her to march."

"You're teaching her to march," said the other woman pensively. "I'm not surprised. The bastards!" she yelled, shaking her fist at the ceiling, "that's all they're after: to make us march, the whole bunch of us, in ranks, just like an army. Why don't they make us goose-step, while they're at it?"

Clumsy with anger she did a brief goose step before the women who had gathered around Rose. Suddenly a strand of gray hair fell into her eyes. She stopped, put a hand to her forehead and disappeared among the spectators.

"Don't sob like that, oh, don't sob like that," someone kept saying behind the crowd where an invisible woman was sobbing, doubled over against a wall of backs.

"Pardon me, but I'd say it's more like little short steps, dance-hall style," said a tough-looking girl, pushing her way into the circle.

She rolled her hips suggestively. There was laughter.

"All right, ladies! What's going on?" shouted a nurse from the end of the room.

The sound of keys, jangling as she ran, announced her arrival.

"I don't like crowds; you know very well I don't like crowds. Out into the yard, all of you!"

She came up to Rose who had not moved.

"I said: all of you!" she said slowly, chewing each word.

"But he is going to come!" cried Rose. How could they mistake her for one of the others? "He is going to come!" she repeated with desperate conviction.

"Then go and wait for him outside," said the nurse, giving her a push.

Outside, a wide stretch of bare ground led to the yellowing lawn, the sterile earth of courtyards, whitewashed with dryness, hard like gritty cement. After a step or two Rose felt the gravel coming through her shoes. She stopped in the full sun. Around her, women were taking off their slippers to empty them, lifting a rough, gray foot, like a horse being shod. Then, with an air of urgency, they started out again, toward some corner of the lawn, to go on chewing the grass of uselessness.

There were some very old patients with snow-white hair, who no longer even had the energy to be crazy, lulled by senility as though it were a cure. Their veined hands on their knees, they sat on the stone benches, while—armed with clipped curses and nails—the madwomen paced back and forth in front of them like a tribe of daughters-in-law.

The city prisons had sent several inmates with dark complexions and brooding, oval faces who sprawled in the grass, their lips sealed by stony silence. They stared straight ahead, defying the brightest sun, with the insolence of gypsies along the highways.

Further on, an orphanage for retarded girls, four or five seventeen- or eighteen-year-olds, with candy ribbons tied as curlers in their blond hair, were beating time with their hands, giggling out of gap-toothed mouths. And the dwarf was there, like an upturned face; you didn't see her; you didn't hear her come; she was there, in your skirts, right up against you, like a ball which has been thrown, stopping, always revealing the same questioning face, large and kinky, with a voice coming

up from under your feet. And above it all the sobbing of the
invisible woman, and the words of her comforter:

"Martha, Martha, don't sob like that, don't sob like that!"
A climbing plant on the sunny asylum wall. . . .

A woman of about sixty with almost snow-white hair and a
soft, worn face came up to Rose. "You've just arrived?" she
asked. "Of course," she went on with a smile, "that was a silly
question. I'm fully aware that you weren't here a minute ago;
I would have noticed you. My name is Mrs. Mingot; yes, even
here, they called me Mrs. . . . I used to teach abroad. I just
arrived myself . . . two years ago, that is. But you'll see,
time does not pass here. Look how new we are."

Rose looked about her, as the old woman's gesture demanded.
She had not retained much from her rapid words, except this
idea of newness, which the old woman ordered her to verify.
The women came and went, or sat in a kind of primitive freedom that Rose had never seen anywhere before. In this narrow
space nothing beckoned to them but themselves. Coming up to
Rose, they assumed singular importance, all buttoned to the
neck in blue linen, armed with all their signs, all their weapons,
intact as on the first day.

"What is your name?" asked Mrs. Mingot.

"Rose." (Are you quite sure? an inner voice murmured in
her ear.) "He is going to come, isn't he!" she exclaimed, desperate with the feeling that everything, even her first name,
might escape her in this state of loneliness.

"Who is going to come?" asked Mrs. Mingot.

Rose didn't answer. She had to be careful with this name,
this last certitude. She must always carry it deep inside her,
make it appear slowly in the hollow of her clasped hands, in
the loneliness of the nights, rouse it again, crush it with her
mouth, involve it endlessly in this debauchery of the heart, this

salty drunkenness of grief, paid with black sleep, with the return of a morning that one should not have lived.

"In any case, today is not visitors' day," pursued Mrs. Mingot with acid gaiety. "Visitors come on Sundays and Thursdays, and besides, you've only arrived. Give yourself time to catch your breath. . . ."

One Sunday morning, long, long ago, they had gone boating. This image now reappeared in Rose's mind. A slight wind had risen in the asylum leaves. It reminded her of the rushing water of a lively stream.

"You're not answering, you seem mute," said Mrs. Mingot. "Do you at least hear what I am saying? Look at me, please, I'm here, I'm talking to you!"

She was now standing before Rose with half-distended mouth and a hurt look in her eyes.

"I so want to see him," stammered Rose painfully.

Reassured, her companion said with eagerness, "You'll see him, don't worry, you'll see him very soon."

She had taken Rose's arm and was pulling her toward the end of the courtyard.

"Okay; let's get this confounded gravel cleaned up!" she shouted to her retinue.

No one heard her. But then, had she really spoken?

"Come, let's go and sit against the wall in the sun," she said to Rose. "We'll have a quiet little chat. You'll be my friend."

"You see," she began, once they had settled down on the ground, "they come. . . . No, don't look for them in the distance. Understand me, I mean it is their function to come, now that we have been exiled. They leave the city on Sundays and Thursdays. Apparently there are extra buses running all up and down this road of compassion. They arrive, bored or distracted, with their guilty consciences, my poor dear, with their shame and pity, and a handful of sugar in their pockets. My only son got tired of it. You'll see, in winter all this is full of mud. One wades ankle-deep in sociology. And we, all dressed in blue, looking all alike. . . . It defies perseverance, it would even defy passion! One day they stop coming. Who is to blame? We died before they did!"

Mrs. Mingot talked on and on. Occasionally she stopped, staring into the distance, her hands open on her knees. At those moments Rose looked at her with curiosity and then once more, closing her eyes, she was swept toward the sky where her lament stretched itself in the wind. Where was he? Why were they so far away from each other? Why?

"How cold it has suddenly become!" said Mrs. Mingot. "Look, Rose, it's actually freezing. . . ."

It was toward evening. She was holding a dead leaf between her fingers, delicate lace. The sun was going down.

"It is freezing," Rose repeated submissively.

She saw a delicate frost cover the trembling leaf and all around, the patinaed stones of the walls, the hardened earth over which the evening was spreading a pale foam of light. She sat among the silent women. She savored the quiet of the hour and the fairy scene of the frost transforming the last light. When the bell rang, she rose calmly, and took a place in the lines before the door that a nurse was unbolting.

"Follow me, don't lose me, Rose! You may even hold my hand," said Mrs. Mingot, pulling her into the dining hall through the flood of women.

Large aluminum pots sat on stoves behind a hedge of nurses.

"Over here! Over here!" called Mrs. Mingot, running between the long tables.

She sat down before Rose could join her, holding both hands on the bench next to her to save the space which she intended for her new companion.

"If you sit near the stoves you'll be served first," she said to Rose who had just sat down beside her. "I've always been

partial to priority, and besides, this cold has made me ravenous.
. . . Smell that: blood sausage tonight; every Wednesday,
burst blood sausage. . . ."

Her smile changed to a pout, but she had already forgotten
her disgust.

"Treguel!" she cried, staring across the table.

The girl called Treguel was one of those who had been danc-
ing rounds a little earlier, in the sun. Now she was waiting for
her plate to be filled . . . with her tin spoon stuck into her
mouth.

"Treguel, will you stop that!" cried Mrs. Mingot, jumping to
her feet.

Nurses were already busy at the end of the table; Mrs. Mingot
turned to them.

"Ladies!" she shouted.

But the hubbub was too great; no one heard her.

"Ladies!" Mrs. Mingot shouted again.

Rose hung her head, petrified with fear of a scandal. Up to
now she had more or less passed unnoticed. For weeks she had
forced herself to be docile, to tiptoe, to keep quiet. She knew
that in this world of punishment in which she had placed herself this was the only way, for her, to "reach the door," to be
with him again.

Two of the nurses had heard Mrs. Mingot's call. They came
over. "Look! Look at her!" said Rose's companion. "And she's
capable of swallowing it. My throat is all in knots just looking at
her. . . ."

"That's enough now, Treguel!" yelled one of the nurses,
tapping her finger against her powdered cheek.

The girl opened round child's eyes and slowly withdrew the
spoon from her mouth.

"Dirty squealer!" said a dark woman at Rose's right. The
nurses had gone away.

"A little advice, dearie," continued the woman, pulling Rose by the sleeve, "watch out for Mrs. Mingot. She squeals. You don't believe it, huh?"

"Leave her alone!" yelled a fat woman with pale cheeks and fluttering eyelids from the other side of the table. "She's frightened. She just got here. Can't you see she's frightened?"

Rose hung her head. There was silence. A ladle of blackish soup was being poured in Rose's plate.

"Lentil soup again!" cried the dark-haired woman.

She didn't feel like eating and clanked her spoon down. One elbow on the table she leaned her cheek on her hand, with a sulky mouth. But soon she got bored. "So you're still frightened," she asked suddenly, again pulling Rose by the sleeve. Rose had just decided to lift her spoon. The soup spilled all over the table and dripped on her dress.

"Oh! This is impossible!" cried Mrs. Mingot who, busy as she was emptying her plate, had seen what had happened.

She raised her hand to catch the eye of one of the nurses and snapped her fingers. This time a murmur of disapproval went up all around the table. The heads of all the women, secretly attached to the same body, welded together at bottom, in the depths of insanity, sitting on their knotted flesh like a king of rats,[1] turned toward Rose and her companion. The murmuring grew louder.

Standing in the middle of the wave, Mrs. Mingot was imploring a white shape. The nurse stopped trying to find the culprit and beat her hands together sharply several times. The women calmed down. The nurse leaned over Rose's shoulder.

"Look here, you're not going to start trouble the minute you arrive," she said to her. "Come on now, eat your soup!"

She pushed a brimming spoon against Rose's lips. Round and obstinate, the metal spoon had the weight and taste of a tongue depressor. Fighting a feeling of nausea, Rose swallowed,

---

1. An abnormality: a litter of rats born with bodies joined, usually by a single tail.

but she hurriedly put the spoon down the minute the nurse—who had put it in her hand—turned her back.

All the women were staring at her, and their joined looks spelled out that label she was so afraid of. What did these women want? Why was she among them? Why wasn't he there? Suddenly she had become the "trouble maker," and they were pointing at her, repeating her name up and down the tables, and each time her name met a blank face, and turned new eyes against her, staring at her, and Mrs. Mingot wouldn't speak to her: she couldn't afford to expose herself; she let Rose bear this dreadful notoriety.

"Stand close to me, Rose," Mrs. Mingot whispered in her ear. "Hold my hand tight, no, tighter than that! Ah, you don't know how to hold on. There, I'll hold your hand. We don't talk on the way to bed."

In ranks they climbed the wide stone steps to the dormitory. In the white tiled corridors the river of women flowed almost noiselessly, uniform, broken only here and there by an arm stretched out as though trying to grip the wall, but finding only a smooth, fleeing plane, it remained suspended a moment in a gesture of farewell. Although the corridors were still lighted, small blue night bulbs were already burning over each door.

They entered a sort of hygienic cloister lined with white-painted beds. In spots the paint was chipped. An iron chair stood beside each bed. The turned-down part of the sheet hid almost all of the blanket, reaching to the foot of the bed. The asylum sheets were exceptionally large, no one knew exactly why, but their extraordinary size never ceased to be disturbing. One felt that one was sleeping in these sheets by suspended sentence, diverting them from their original destination (suggested by a slight odor of formaldehyde): operating rooms, linen-lined bath tubs, ice wraps, morgue shrouds. One did not live in them. Hard and stiff, they surrounded a sleep that was entirely wrapped up in itself. "Well, you're not too badly placed," said Mrs. Mingot to Rose whom a nurse had just shown to her bed. "You're next to Gertrude, and on your left you have the little spoon eater. Tomorrow I'll arrange to get the bed next to yours."

She waved a hurried goodbye just as the nurse who had gone to the door and turned with a stern look was about to tell her to get back to her place. The women undressed hastily and slipped into their beds without putting on nightgowns to replace their gray linen shirts. Only one of them cried out, one short, sharp cry, like those that rise from a birdhouse or from trees when night falls with a noise of crumpled wings.

"Tsk! Tsk! Tsk!" clicked the nurse with the tip of her tongue.

"Shut up, Roubillot!" yelled someone.

"Tsk! Tsk! Tsk!" went the nurse again, standing at the door, waiting to turn off the light.

An electric switch snapped and the half-light reigned, bluish and filled with sighs, more terrible for those who, at the bottom of their constant fright, anticipated this daily execution that condemned them to suffering until morning, less kind than darkness to those who were tormented mostly by daylight phantoms.

On the next morning and the days that followed, Rose, accompanied by Mrs. Mingot, returned to her screen of light, to that sunny place along the wall where, on the first evening, the chill of the depths had taken them by surprise.

"He is coming, surely he'll come today," Rose repeated each time Mrs. Mingot forced her out of silence. Should I have let him come to me, the first time? It was evening, I was scared of every bush, although I kept laughing, and we were still a hundred yards from the boat. It all happened yesterday, only yesterday. And we'll begin again!

"Sh," said Mrs. Mingot, "shhhhh! Be quiet, Rose, don't say a word. That's from the opera 'The Dragoons of Villars.' At the Red Cross I had a cook who used to sing all day long His name was Ruprecht. He sang in German. I know German; Russian, too. . . ."

They were sitting on the ground; Rose kept silent and listened to her companion's endless monologue. Mrs. Mingot unrolled her past, image after image of a far-away reality of which Rose began to be conscious again. All the human feelings: first pity ("Just think, that was in nineteen forty-three, pity was dressed in red"), then goodness ("never returned, carried off in the coat of a begging thief"), love, ah yes, love, but also maternal love, anger, fear, hatred. "The whole long list, see," Mrs. Mingot said very often, "let me tell you. . . ."

Now she was talking of bodily miseries: cold; but it was very hard for her to call up the notion of cold sitting there against that burning wall: "You saw how it was, yesterday, and this is June! I'm sure if you dug into the ground here you'd find frost, just like they find coal in other places. That's what makes me think that something must have happened, that we are perhaps no longer alive," she whispered with sinister delight: ". . . not altogether living, not altogether flesh." She also talked of fatigue, of hunger; and while, a little earlier, the description of love and pity had not moved Rose, the idea of hunger brought light to her eyes. The asylum meals were skimpy.

"At the Red Cross canteen, when they boiled potatoes, they always mashed them with a big pounder. Of course no milk. But to make up for it, lots of fat. Ah! And I can tell you: lots of fat!"

"And bread? What about bread?" asked Rose in a slightly hoarse voice.

At last she was talking sense. Smiling Mrs. Mingot tipped her white head back against the hot wall and let Rose wait for an answer.

"The bread was supplied by the commissary. Biscuit. Careful now: in the exact sense of the term: twice baked. It made the crust thick and crunchy. The ration was a loaf per person: all you could eat, that is. . . ."

"I'm hungry," murmured Rose.

Mrs. Mingot leaned over her: "When he comes, the one you miss so much, he'll bring you bread, all sorts of goodies. That's all they come for. The dead must be fed. But, to be quite frank with you, I don't think he'll come. It's too far, you see, too far, and besides, to get here he might have to cross a river, and no bridges, all kinds of obstacles. And besides, who knows? Do you deserve his visit? Perhaps you've been unfaithful, nasty? You're not listening!"

No, Rose wasn't listening.

"Come, we'll go in," said Mrs. Mingot dejectedly, and took her arm. "This heat is killing me."

Dodging the nurses, they slipped into the building and walked slowly down the white corridors.

"Here, over here!" whispered Mrs. Mingot who had gone ahead of Rose and had stopped in front of a window. "Come look!"

There was Section Three, invisible from anywhere else, so well hidden, so secret that this window opening upon it, exactly like all the other windows that lighted the corridor, seemed pierced by a sharper sun. In Section Three lived the wilder cases.

"They're the wild ones," said Mrs. Mingot. "Look at them! I sometimes have the impression that they're calling me. Look, that one who is holding out her arms as though you were her child. Don't turn your head away! Believe me, they are the mothers of revelation. Oh! I feel so sorry for them. So terribly sorry! They feel everything, they suffer everything, everything goes through them, all the stakes, all the swords, all the knives that get stuck into living flesh all over the place. . . . Look, they're gathering. Why yes, they're giving them soup. . . . Soup, just like that, at five o'clock in the afternoon! Rose, I have a funny feeling, come on, let's get out of here! Something

is going on. I bet they're getting ready to transfer them somewhere tonight, *abtransportieren,* you know what I mean, come
on, let's go!"

Rose remained motionless. The small courtyard in front of
the Section Three building was now deserted. A very high wire
mesh closed it in like a bird house. There was white sun everywhere. A woman came out into the light and then (probably
they were all still there?) ran back in and the façade closed
again on the drama of the besieged, on a final silence, mounted
very high at the peak of a scream.

"What are you doing here?" a nurse asked Mrs. Mingot as
she was passing with her antiseptic odor, jangling keys and
powdered cheeks. "I was afraid she was getting too much sun,"
answered Mrs. Mingot smiling. "You know she's not well yet,"
she added in a low voice, pointing to Rose. "A little while ago,
outside, I thought she was going to start screaming any moment. . . ."

"Really?"

The nurse came up to Rose.

"Rose Schmidt, lift up your head, let me see your eyes," she
said gently, taking Rose by the arm.

Rose looked at her squarely. The nurse decided to smile as
though hoping to tame her, and finally was the first to turn her
eyes away.

"All right, back outside!" she told Mrs. Mingot dryly before
walking off.

Every morning it was the same with the doctor on duty.
Even he couldn't stand for long the painful look with which
Rose answered every human gesture. He couldn't be blamed for
this incarceration, which the most superficial clinical observation amply justified, nor for the illness he was laboring to cure,
and yet he turned his eyes away, feeling suddenly responsible,
in the chalky morning light, for this nakedness, this hurt, this
loneliness.

They had to get up at six o'clock. They swallowed their bowl of malt, ate their slice of dry bread and stayed seated in the dining room waiting for the sun to light the yard. Among them those who underwent daily treatment waited for the nurse's call. Rose didn't know whether or not she, too, might be called and from the first day she had joined this silent, badly defined minority, composed of slightly haggard women who sat at the table, making their hand slide slowly over the wood, interminably, untiringly treading, far from themselves, furtive messages of fear. Near them, Mrs. Mingot was silent, her eyes large with waiting.

"If they call me, I won't budge," she had said to Rose. "They'll be obliged to carry me in. And then, goodbye life, goodbye love . . ."

The large glass door at the end of the room was going to open on one of those early-morning destinies that never brought you anything worth while. Isn't it disturbing that people on the other side of the walls are already up at this hour, putting cloths on tables?

The call was slow in coming, the sun slow in shining over the walls, the women remained silent, pacified by fear. And then came the moment when, in the sky, powers changed, night balanced day. Tics slackened, nerves relaxed. It was the moment when inner voices no longer shouted threats, when breathing eased, when knotted throats untied themselves, when an interminable thread of saliva ran from idiot mouths, when the feeble did not hold back their urine and when, in a corner, a lost woman in the midst of this pitiful herd wept noiselessly from closed eyes.

Toward the end of July the heat chased Rose and her companion from their favorite place against the wall. Mrs. Mingot had stood it as long as she could: she was afraid that Rose might escape her somewhere else. . . . For hours she would watch her weep, not without some pleasure, finding in her tears unreserved approval, a justification of her theories of hopelessness and hell. Nevertheless she decided to look for a little shade. "If we stay here, you'll turn into a 'Section Three,' " she said to Rose. "They'd separate us. . . ."

They went over and sat in the middle of the lawn, among the other women who, for the last few days, had been crossing beyond the syringa bushes. But in this newly conquered space the asylum community caught up with them again, noisier and more disorderly than ever. From time to time Roubillot screamed, as she did in the dormitory: her peacock's cry, a break in the silent massacre which raged in her heart day and night. The dark-haired woman whom they called Redempcion somersaulted over the heads of the others and then collapsed on the grass, showing her thighs, eyes closed in a sort of ambiguous dizziness. Gertrude crawled across the lawn. Others sang, with a blade of grass ringed around a finger; the world was immense between the syringa bushes. Suddenly it was the slope of a hill where grass brides screeched out a chorale in falsetto voices; it was the heart of a black forest where Roubillot screamed. An odor of baked laurels hung in the air. Lying on her back, her eyes closed and her arms stretched out palms down against the ground, Rose felt the summer earth, the great luminous day ripple away from her to blurred horizons. Her white smock dazzling in the sunlight, a nurse came across the lawn and clapped her hands.

"Ah, that's right, visitors' day today," said Mrs. Mingot and hurriedly helped Rose to her feet. "When it's too hot, they don't use the parlor; they come out here on the grass, and we get locked in. . . ."

At the door, several women were pleading with the nurse. They never had any visitors and they wanted to bring chairs down from the dormitory as the visitors would need them. It was a job worth fighting for. The men spoke words different from those here. The women wore print dresses. Freedom gave them all the elegance and grace of riches.

"I don't want to see them, you know," said Mrs. Mingot to Rose when they had come into the hall, "I know only too well what illusions they represent and what treason they bring with them. Don't leave me, Rose! I haven't told you the end of my story with the Hungarians yet, you know, the story I was telling you this morning. Come over here, close to me. . . . What are you looking at over there, Rose?"

The other women seemed more nervous, too. The heat made them tense. During the last several days, whenever they clustered together, madness took over: not noisily, but insidiously, crawling like vermin that they might have been passing from one to the other.

"I have the feeling that she'll come today," said a young woman next to Louise.

There were so many freckles on her face, so much hope, that Rose and several other women turned to look at her.

"Yes, certainly my mother is coming!" repeated the young woman with an air of ecstasy. Mrs. Mingot shrugged. "Your mother! How do you know? I'm asking you: what do you know about it? And even if she did come: Here, my child, I've brought you chocolate and some hard-boiled eggs, a real travel basket. It is a long trip. I know, my child, I know, but we must be patient. Patience! Tastes like sand. Here you are in the middle of the desert, and they tell you: 'Eat some sand!' "

Outside, the gravel was crunching under the feet of the first visitors. "Don't listen to her!" a white-haired inmate shouted to the young woman. "I'm sure she'll come. I'll let you know when I hear her step. I can always tell their step when they're old like I am. Don't worry, I'm listening. . . ."

She hid her face in her hands, while the young woman remained wide-eyed before her hope, which was going to sink, she could feel it, and already she was swallowing her tears.

The nurse opened the door, called a name, and the chosen woman stood up and walked toward her with the exalted expression of someone who has rediscovered his secret. Mrs. Mingot had fallen asleep. Rose went over to the window and stood behind the women who were gathered there, watching. Perhaps he would come today?

A man dressed in black passed right in front of their faces, saw them, bowed furtively and hurried toward the lawn. Then came two fat women, carrying black oilcloth shopping bags. They were red and sweaty. Here, everyone was pale; one never perspired. Little Treguel stuck her tongue out at them and they walked off. The nurse kept opening and closing the door.

"Blanche Premontier! Adèle Caillon! Julia Vuillaume! Martha Benoux!"

The woman advanced; most often silent, she submitted to effusive greetings, with her arms limp at her sides and, after the visitor had sat down, she, too, sat down on one of the iron chairs her companions had eagerly brought.

To escape the silence and the embarrassment, packages were hastily taken out of linen bags, out of old leather briefcases, and unwrapped; in this silence of surprise and mutual affliction, one clutched at the helpfulness, the humble eloquence of these primitive offerings. Then the eating began, often shared with a good will bordering on disgust by the visitor who tried to put the madwoman at ease, to let her bask in the warmth of complicity. Then, eagerly peeling an orange for her: "I think we're in luck, they seem to be nice and juicy," he began a conversation.

From the window Rose and her companions caught snatches of sentences, torn from a long and colorless family chronicle.

"Ernestine is expecting a baby, in January, probably. . . ."

He stretched his news with brief comments, marked by a sort of serene resignation. "Ah yes, life goes fast!" he nodded and quickly out of the corner of his eye, treacherously, he spied on the patient's reactions. What sort of trap was this?

"But . . . you remember Ernestine, your cousin who married a Gillet," the messenger repeated softly, discouraged by his wife's silence. "The one who lives near the post office, next to the drugstore. . . ."

And little by little he got caught in the absurd universe of Ernestine whom his insistence was giving new dimensions.

"So you're still in love with her?"

He restrained himself.

"What are you talking about? Please, Camilla, pay a little attention to your words. You know very well that Ernestine. . . ."

Ernestine again. He couldn't get out of it. He would leave here, stamped with Ernestine. The trap he had laid was closing in on him. Close your eyes, the story flows like an undammed stream. . . .

"Is she crying?" asked a woman nearby.

"No, Ma'am, she is pretending to be asleep," answered the man wearily. "She used to do that even before she fell ill. It's as though one weren't there, as though one didn't exist."

He shook his head, wrapped up his gifts and placed them on the knees of the pretending sleeper. "There is no Ernestine in my life. . . ."

Many inmates remained fiercely silent in the presence of their visitors. Their mouths became powdered with flour as they bit into a cake, held in both hands, with the same voracity with which, the rest of the time, they threw themselves upon certain words, upon certain images, since they no longer belonged to a world fed on reason. The visitors looked at them, smiling at first, but soon, as the woman stuffed larger and larger pieces into her mouth, their approval stretched to a look of worried surprise. Anyone else would have choked, but no, she looked at them, calmly, her throat bloated like a goiter. Don't worry! She would never swallow anything so big, so round as her suffering. . . .

When she had finished, they tilted back their iron chairs,

let their eyes wander about with casual interest: they were taking in the facts. After having seemed oppressive for a long time, the asylum had become an excursion similar to those on which, during their vacations, they went to visit "curiosities of nature," rocks pierced by cascades, blue-walled grottoes, dolmens where the wind moans like an animal: here, the creations of insanity were offered to their sight, it was, they felt, a little more interesting than intertwining trees. Standing with two feet planted squarely on the shore, they watched the waves foam at the edge of the sea where it bordered on the shifting sands. . . .

Listlessly Rose listened to their conversations; mechanically she observed their secret movements.

Mrs. Mingot's words came back to her: these people were perhaps in reality nothing but phantoms of memory, persons born of regret to give this simulacrum of life. When you examined them closely, their very naturalness betrayed them. At certain moments they really overdid it.

What a bad actor Ernestine's false lover was: he had placed oranges in his wife's lap. Her eyes were still closed, and every time she seemed about to move or breathed a little more heavily, he hastily put his hand on the oranges to keep them from rolling to the ground. When equilibrium returned—had it been disturbed at all?—he withdrew his hand with extreme slowness, a lingering caress.

An even worse actress was the fat woman in the black spangled dress who was sitting with a girl with a ribbon in her hair. She was blowing into a small goldbeater's skin with a sort of whistle valve. As the balloon grew fatter, clearer and more transparent, the cheeks of the fat woman, distended with effort, paled and bulged. At last she pulled the valve out of her mouth and, letting the balloon empty itself with a sort of monotoned meow, she looked at her daughter with moist eyes and smiled. It was what one calls "a pitiful smile" and that wasn't any more acceptable, that fat woman holding this collapsed, wrinkled piece of skin in her fingers, and who was going to start all over again because probably a light had come into her daughter's eyes and who, for a change of taste, would finally pull some gingerbread men out of a brown paper bag. Her daughter was at least twenty.

And the indifferent ones, the architects who were endlessly measuring the asylum buildings with their eyes, allowing themselves to admit once again with visible satisfaction that we did not want for anything, all the stones were neatly in their places, and plentiful, one had to admit, the city did not stint when it came to stones. Play acting, all of it.

"He is waiting for me somewhere else," thought Rose, "he is real, but how can I call him, hear his answer, direct myself toward him, join him?"

The visiting hour was almost over. The visitors left and waved their hands over their heads, sometimes even without turning back.

"Well, what has this performance taught you?" asked Mrs. Mingot dryly, taking Rose's arm. "He didn't come, obviously, and you didn't recognize anybody in this excuse for a crowd. They have all been carefully screened, let me assure you, not one of them could bring you the slightest help."

The doors of the big hall were pushed open again; they went out into the yard. The women had not yet taken up their places on the lawn. They were standing in groups, or alone, depending on whether the event had raised their hopes or shattered them.

"Well, what did I tell you!" said Mrs. Mingot to the young woman with freckles. "She didn't come, huh?"

The young woman was standing at the door; her eyes were red; she did not seem to hear. Mrs. Mingot left her to her dreaming and pulled Rose away. "See what a bad habit hope is. . . ."

Near them, Gertrude who had had a visit, was talking loudly to a circle of women: "They swore that it was so. Five hundred yards from here, and you know what they said: 'It should have been put further away.' They thought I hadn't heard it. I asked them: 'And why should it have been put further away?' They looked at each other, and the fat one who always talks answered: 'Well, because it is a fair . . . !'"

"He promised me, oh I don't know what you call it, what do you call it, something absolutely marvelous," said a woman with real tears of joy in her eyes. "God knows, he must have worked day and night to buy it for me. 'You'll have it, you'll have it,' he kept saying, 'you'll have it, you'll have it. . . .'"

They laughed and laughed, biting on their hands, stamping their feet, and the woman with the present raised her brimming eyes toward the sky where her joy continued to exist.

Toward evening the agitation died down; copper-colored clouds had climbed the sky. Nurses could be heard calling the time to each other across the sections: "Twenty of!" A white smock disappeared behind black leaves. Evening: would hope ever be born again? A little later, after they had gone to bed, the sounds of a country fair came over the trees and the asylum walls.

"Hear that? Hear that? What did I tell you!" cried Gertrude, sitting up in bed.

The stalls of the fair had been thrown up at a certain distance from the asylum gates. Only a vague, oozing music filtered through, punctuated by metallic sounds from the shooting galleries. In the windows the iron bars and the leaves stood out against a sky that was hardly any paler than usual.

"I'm going!" Gertrude declared loudly, encouraged by the total absence of nurses; they were probably watching the fair from the attic windows. "Yes, as you see me standing here, I'm going to take a look at the fair. After all, the fair is for every-body!" she exclaimed fiercely, as though sensing objections in the shadows. "Once I saw an ex-convict at a fair. They brought him the ducks they had won at the shooting stands and whack!

he'd cut their heads off. You should have seen him! No one dared make a move. The fair isn't France, you know!"

"Yeah, she'll try it all right. I'm sure the guards have guns. . . ." It was Mrs. Mingot's voice.

"Shit guns!" cried Gertrude.

She bounced out of bed and started to dress.

"What's she doing?" came a worried voice from the other end of the dormitory.

"What's she doing?" asked a woman without lifting her head in a voice of great sickness. "My God, why did they put out my eyes?"

"And the wall?" said someone. "How will you get across the wall?"

Gertrude explained that she had a long, heavy nail, which she had stolen from the masons some weeks ago, and that she would stick it in between two bricks to give herself a grip and hoist herself to the top.

"She has a nail," reported the echo, "she has a nail as big as a dagger. . . ."

"A dagger," affirmed the echo, returning from the other end of the dormitory.

Near Rose, in the aisle which separated the two beds, Gertrude finished getting dressed. One could hear her whistling breath. Meanwhile, around her, the excitement reached a peak; faced with the gravity of the event, each woman rediscovered a little of her sanity.

Finally Gertrude left the dormitory. She was walking on tiptoe, a finger on her lips; she had forgotton to tie the belt of her asylum dress. Mrs. Mingot pointed it out with a ferocious little laugh, and by this detail alone one felt that Gertrude was lost. In the distance the fair was probably going strong. The noise had grown louder. But perhaps it was only an approaching storm: one must watch out for everything in this world.

Women got up to go to the toilets, dawdled in the dormitory, kept swinging the hall doors. Mrs. Mingot came over to Rose's bed.

"I'm afraid for you, you are in the next bed. They'll question you, grill you. God, what a dreadful night!"

She squeezed Rose's arm through the covers and headed toward the hall door.

In the dormitory the women continued to talk about the fair:

"That's what happens at fairs," said a voice lost in darkness. "I had never trusted those dark alleys between the wagons; and the little gypsy girl who was doing the split, do you imagine he didn't look at her? I was only good enough for slapping, and when he went over to the shooting gallery with some two hundred people around it, I stood there like a fool watching him aim at a red-painted iron pigeon, and what did I suddenly understand: he was aiming at my hand! I was wearing red gloves that day, he was aiming at my hand, at my hand. . . ."

"Come, Bertha, you're exaggerating! Go to sleep. . . ."

"What a silly idea to have taken him to the fair. A man just moves a finger, and everything goes. . . ."

"My hand," the woman whined once more, mechanically, hardly believing it herself. Then, one after the other, they fell silent, carried away by the merry-go-round, their own silent merry-go-round to which they clung each night.

Quite a long time had gone by when a nurse came into the dormitory and snapped on all the lights.

Soon afterward Gertrude appeared, held between two other nurses. Strands of wet hair hung down either side of her thin face. She was wrapped in a sheet down to her ankles, walking barefoot with quick, short steps.

She was crying, her chin on her chest; every sob made her shoulders heave; when she reached her bed the nurses took the sheet off and dressed her in a shirt. The skin of her body was whipped red from the shower, from wet towels thrown with

washerwoman energy. She was still breathless. The nurses put
her to bed, lifting her up by her feet and under the arms: they
put her in the grave.

The nurses talked on their way out. The last one slammed
the door of the partition which separated them from the dormitory and soon all the lights went out; sounds from the fair
could still be heard. Later everything fell silent and it rained.
Rose sat up then and edged her hand toward Gertrude's bed.
She was still crying and so deeply lost in her torment that the
presence of this hand did not surprise her, if she sensed it at
all. At this point, no matter what, it could only be for the
better. Rose moved her hand toward Gertrude's forehead.
Sitting up suddenly, Gertrude bit her.

The incidents of that night left hardly any traces. The next
morning very few women seemed to remember. Half aloud,
they accused Mrs. Mingot of having squealed on Gertrude. A
pointless accusation: Gertrude was not sent to Section Three;
nor was she disciplined, or even questioned, and what's more,
she, herself, didn't seem in any way surprised at this. It was
understood that here life was erased, memory abandoned. Only
Mrs. Mingot tried to revive the incident. The noises of the fair
were gone. It was a weekday, at noon.

"You see how powerful they are," Mrs. Mingot said to
Louise. "They made a whole fair move away. And to think
some people still go around imagining that they have rights!
That they'll leave here, one day, that they'll escape the regula-
tions! No, no, Rose, we are their creatures and the world
belongs to them. They conjure up visits for us, and the sounds
of a fair, and then they erase it all. The strategy of bait, and
that's what they call life. You don't realize how happy they
are to hear you say that word. That's all they want. . . ."

But Rose said nothing. She was lying flat on her back in the
grass. She was thinking of Paul. How he loved her! She would
like to prove it to all these doubters. . . .

"Wake up, Rose," said Mrs. Mingot, "here they come. Sit up! Sit up; don't make a spectacle of yourself."

Rose sat up and looked about her, plucking a handful of grass.

"They're heading straight for us," said Mrs. Mingot. "It's you they're coming for. I'll leave you. But please, my dear, defend yourself. Don't let them take you away, Rose. Promise me, promise your old friend."

She scuttled off, her shoulders hunched. The men were coming closer. Rose recognized their grave faces because, from time to time, these men came wandering through the section to question some of the women. They all talked at the same time, without raising their voices, then fell silent and took notes on a pad.

"Who are you?" a woman asked them, desperate with daring.

"Who are we?" answered one of them. "But you know very well, we are the people who are going to let you go home very soon, if you are reasonable and obedient. . . ."

"Oh, but I am obedient!" cried the woman, full of sudden hope. "Ask the head nurse! She thinks I'm the best one here!"

The four men continued their walk, stopping when their conversation became animated, walking on again, deep in thought, tormented by the objections they would soon have to express, with a frown and a crooked forefinger rubbing the side of their noses. But the woman did not let them get away; she trailed them, her face tense, her mouth spewing formulas of servility, obsequious words, bits of accusation. Another minute and she would be on her knees.

A nurse finally decided to intervene and, caught in the game of obedience, the woman let herself be led away without protest; this was the final test, of course. They were watching her obey. It was only when she arrived in the hall and the door closed behind her that she understood that they had tricked her, that they were not going to call her back and grant her their nod of approval. She pressed her cheeks against the greenish windowpane and watched them walk away, her face drowned in childhood grief.

They stopped near Rose who remained seated on the grass.

"I remember her," one of them said. "I saw her back at the admission. Nothing terrible, it seems."

"No, just a confused state, too much strain plus a sentimental trauma," replied a man with a white crew cut. "We have left her alone and she is slowly coming out of it by herself. Perhaps the real problem is going to start now. . . ."

"Don't talk to me about those problems," sighed one of the two men who had been silent until now. "They give me more trouble than anything that happens before. They ask me to cure human beings. But three times out of four I am useless. I'd have to cure their lives as well!"

"Yes, it is my impression that, in her case, the second part of the program is the most important," the white-haired man said again.

"Where is Paul, my husband?" asked Rose, getting up.

She was talking to the man who had spoken last, and not without a certain intention of violence but, finding his eyes and seeing the sympathy in them, she felt lost and started to tie and untie the ends of her belt in front of her dress.

"Your husband," replied the man, studying his nails, "your husband. . . ." His hand no longer interested him and his eyes returned to Rose's face. "I'll soon find out where he is and I'll let you know, yes," he continued with suspicious cordiality, "one of these days the two of us must have a nice little chat. I'll send for you."

Since the beginning of this exchange one of the men had been watching the speaker with a questioning look. He noticed it as he turned away from Rose. He made a face. Rose saw it. It was the sort of face a doctor makes on his way out of the sickroom to say that things are serious or, at least, not too good.

"It's banal and complicated all at once," he murmured, "a broken marriage, he left her; it happens every day, but the unusual part is her refusal. . . ."

He walked on and continued to talk to the others. "Obviously he can't ask for a divorce as long as she's in here!" he exclaimed at one point. "But that's probably the least of his worries. . . ."

Suddenly he feared that he had spoken too loudly and turned back to see whether Rose had overheard. She was staring at him, wide-eyed. That's when he noticed her wounded hand.

"What happened?" he asked, going up to Rose. "What happened to your hand?"

"Gertrude bit me," replied Rose and began to suck her wound.

"I can see you smiling, yes, I can see you smiling, my dear President," said the man with the white crew cut, turning toward one of his companions. "You are probably thinking of what I said a moment ago: that the asylum cures. And in your mind you answer: yes, but this woman is desperate because she doesn't see her husband; locked inside these walls she goes up to Gertrude, and Gertrude bites her. And I'll throw more oil on your fire: Do you know what happened last night to Gertrude? She tried to escape and they caught her. I might add that, in these cases, the nurses are rather firm. And so you say: how can the asylum cure anybody? It's a hell. . . ."

"It is you who are using the word 'hell,' not I. I wouldn't go quite so far," answered the man they called President.

"Well, I authorize you to go that far," said the other. "Let's assume that this is hell: sometimes there is no screaming—although not always—no frenzy and of course no torture. It may seem lukewarm, vague, dull, but hell burns with a low flame like those apartment heaters that you can touch without burning your hand, but they're suffocating. In short, this is a prison, a place of punishment—a hell, to use that word again. And this atmosphere of punishment imposes itself.

"The best would be, of course, if each one of these women, surprised by the onslaught of fate, recognized the need to hold court in herself. How much time we would save! She would soon discover that the hell is inside, that there exists, within her, far away, a state of grace, a deserted paradise. Please note the word 'deserted.' Insanity is often an evasion, a desertion, thus, very often related to guilt. Note that, when I speak of hell, I refer to this young woman in particular. As long as she refuses to accept the truth, her truth. . . . But I want her to find it by herself. . . . Yes, I assure you! She knows it perfectly!" he exclaimed, in answer to one of the other men's questions.

He stepped aside, getting out of Rose's way. She ran off. Hell! Out of reach, she slowed down and wandered about the sunny courtyard which was treacherous, too, like the rest of the world, a playground for innumerable evils.

Someone touched her arm.

"Ah, Mrs. Mingot!" said Rose, clutching her companion's shoulder.

"What did they say to you? What did they do to you?" asked Mrs. Mingot with a sort of radiant pity.

"We're in hell," said Rose with a frown, as though this word had been hiding a problem.

"Aha! In hell! Why yes, indeed! A fine discovery you've made there, my dear girl!" replied Mrs. Mingot. "Your old friend has been telling you that every day, but you didn't believe her. Others have to come and break the big news: we're in hell!"

"No, no, he didn't want that," murmured Rose to herself. "Hell doesn't exist. Not for me! Not for me!"

"What are you saying, Rose? I don't understand," said Mrs. Mingot.

Rose looked through her: her eyes were wide open—on her memories.

"Come, I'll tell you, I'll prove it to you!" she cried after a moment, pulling Mrs. Mingot after her with sudden authority.

The sun was dropping. They went to sit in their regular place against the wall. For a moment Rose kept her face in her hands, then she raised her head. Her eyes fixed a distant point in space, like people who perfectly remember a certain date but seem to go on looking for it way back in their memory, because they want to measure the road they've traveled since then.

Finally she named the year and the season of that year when her story began, and she began to talk. She was going to talk for a long, a very long time. For whole days, whole weeks, for months. She was going to talk in the morning, while waiting for day to come into the dining room, waiting among her companions half awake in their insanity, sitting fearfully, pressed one against the other on the benches. She was going to talk in the boredom of the autumn days, when it is only five o'clock and the rain beats against the foggy windows. She was going to talk at night, at the metal-covered table that offered an endless succession of boneless meals, gray gruels, lukewarm soups, tasteless food that seemed to be prechewed. And she was going to talk on their way to the dormitory, before she pulled the rough, formaldehyde-scented sheets over her forgotten body. And even then her monologue would only seem to stop. Eyes closed, on the edge of sleep, she went over and over the events of her life. It was not simple reverie, an easy stream of images. Her memories were arranged in the order of a legal claim: through them ran the thread of her defense.

In her confidences to Mrs. Mingot, Rose dwelled upon unimportant incidents, all of which belonged to the beginning of her conjugal idyll. She obviously felt little desire to risk herself beyond that. Perhaps her memory simply did not go any further? Now that she had rediscovered this memory, how precisely, how frantically she re-created this happy phase of her past! Details abounded. A door was opened. A door was closed. One day they had lost a key. . . . Mrs. Mingot held up her hand and nodded: no need to go any further. She was already well enough informed.

"That was a warning, my dear," she declared. "You're unforgivable not to have understood."

"But what was there to understand?" asked Rose.

She plunged her face between her hands. Her thoughts were wandering. And then, winter was interferring now. Winter was a terribly mental season here, because then insanity was cloistered. Parked in the half-light of the room, largely deprived of movement, the women passionately played with signs and superstitions.

This was probably due to the influence of several merchants of the supernatural, palm readers and clairvoyants whom an excess of spiritual effort and exploration of the beyond had led to the asylum where they continued to practice their obscure religion. They had quickly made disciples, because there was hardly a patient who did not feel the need to hold some identifiable power responsible for her visions and "voices," to give her delirium a place in a superior, well-ordered hierarchy.

Occultism was less an aggregate of beliefs than an enterprise of justification. It was good to know that tables turned under the hands of spiritualists, because it explained once and for all any form of dizziness one might experience. Magic legitimized the instability of objects, the birth of phantoms, the persecutions of invisible, hollow-voiced prosecutors. Dog-eared, greasy tarot decks passed from hand to hand:

"Well, dearie, shall I do a full reading for you?" asked a fat woman, taking a seat at the table across from a quiet young girl who had arrived only recently.

The muteness of the newcomers, still paralyzed with fear, the sort of dull stupor they had kept when they left life, always attracted the fat mamas whose eyes, after several years in the asylum, shone again with a malicious light, almost a glimmer of sanity. The girl stared straight ahead, her hand smoothing out the greasy metal table top in front of her.

"Let's go; take your paws out of the way and cut!" the fat mama ordered gently, smoothing her cards. "Nothing more reliable. . . ."

Several women came wandering over.

"Come on, let's take a look," said Mrs. Mingot, getting up. Since Rose had begun to talk, Mrs. Mingot had become more turbulent, more interested in the community life. Since she no longer had "the floor," she was looking for other distractions.

Her monologue had been interrupted. Rose didn't want to move. She let her old friend go and leaned her head against the glossy wall, a welcome truce that permitted her to go back over the points of her defense and verify them one by one with a detachment which the speed and the unexpected dovetailing of facts did not always permit while she was "telling herself" to Mrs. Mingot. Who could deny it? Our understanding was deep and complete. One rarely sees a couple as unified as we were . . . as we still are. No matter what they do, we are still those two united beings. . . .

She was going to cry again, she was already crying while laughter burst out at the table where ten women were now leaning over the fortune teller.

"A blond young man! Did you hear that? The cards predict the visit of a blond young man. We'll know all about it!" they shouted around the girl who was paying no attention to her own destiny.

"A little quiet please, ladies!" ordered Big Mama Houdin.

They calmed down. There was only the clicking noise of Mama Houdin's forefinger, jumping from card to card.

"One, two, three, four: Death! One, two, three, four: Death!" a skinny, white-haired woman began to chant, rising suddenly to her full height. She left the table, beating time with her hands.

Voices rose up behind her: "Hey you! Shut up!"

Once more all heads bent over the cards. But the signal had been given. Already everything was echoing the incantation that continued, all the way down at the other end of the dining room, where the white-haired woman paced back and forth, clapping her hands.

"Spades again!"

There was the ace of spades, a black heart on a stem. They stared at the girl with sharp curiosity.

"You're going to die, do you hear!" cried Redempcion, shaking the girl as one shakes a sleeper. "Are you deaf? Show your palm! She's going to die, huh?"

Puffed up with glory, her face shiny with satisfaction and sweat, Big Mama Houdin nodded her head in agreement without even bothering to read the girl's palm which Redempcion was holding out to her. Slowly she gathered up the cards, without paying any more attention to the girl who was looking at her with eyes already full of tears, and wringing her hands.

"She's speechless, imagine what a shock!" said the women, examining her very closely, and still more closely, fixedly, ready to touch her porcelain cheek with their fingers.

The hubbub pulled Rose out of her thoughts. "Who is she? What's her name?" she asked Mrs. Mingot who was coming back with an excited, radiant face. "I don't think I know her."

"Iphigenia. She arrived two days ago. You know, Houdin dealt her cards very carefully, conscientiously. She even seemed inspired for once. Of course you never can tell with these fat people, still, the evidence is there: it seems that the girl is going to die. . . ."

The girl had gotten up and was spinning around under the unbearable stares of the madwomen. She had been condemned unanimously, and Rose, who saw nothing but a cruel game in

this verdict, an absurd ritual, supported the sentence by her
immobility, by her indifference. Besides, she no longer felt any
pity. She would do nothing to console the unfortunate young
woman who was wandering about the room in the grayish light.
Her own past was still devoured by night; it needed all her
attention, and besides, a sort of physical repulsion excluded her
a little more each day from those whose fate she shared.

Their physical degradation hindered contact even more than
their unbalanced minds. Insanity soured their breath, left a
slight odor of urine and sweat in their clothes, swelled their
breasts with ridiculous ardor, moistened their lips with constant
drooling, spoiled all sexuality and in the folds of their shaggy
dresses it made the women sit on a small toad.

"You see, my dear. . . ." said Mrs. Mingot.

But Redempcion had come up to them. "Do you know the
prayers for the dead?" she asked Rose.

Rose shrugged her shoulders. She was not religious.

But nevertheless she dreamily repeated Redempcion's words:
"The prayers for the dead. . . ."

They were the kind of words that suddenly uncover the sea,
the black night; the wind beating the water like a curtain.

"I know them!" replied Mrs. Mingot. "I've sat through
enough wakes, during the war! We commend to Thee, O Lord,
the soul of Thy handmaid, dead to this world, may she live only
for Thee and may Thy infinite compassion wipe away. . . ."

"Okay," said Redempcion, her voice suddenly grave. "It's
for the new girl. Houdin said so. She doesn't have much more
time. We've made her sit down. We're not going to let her die
like a dog!" she yelled, clenching her fists. "Who knows, maybe
tomorrow they'll take her away, all stiff and dead and shove
her into the morgue without a drop of holy water. You believe
in God. Well, let me tell you, so do I. I, too, am the soul of
Thy handmaid, come on, let's get going. . . ."

Mrs. Mingot hesitated.

"After all, I do have the right," she said to Rose, trying to convince herself, "after all, I represent the Red Cross. . . ."

She got up and followed Redempcion.

The girl was sitting at the other end of the room, guarded by three women like a prisoner awaiting execution.

"What's the use of looking?" Rose said to herself. Anything that did not concern her history left her unmoved. She tried to convince herself. And yet, there were moments. . . . Again she let her head fall back against the glossy wall. But soon voices rose at the other end of the room, voices she did not recognize. She opened her eyes. The girl was sitting on a bench. She was absolutely immobile. Four women were kneeling at her feet.

"Let's start again," said one of them, turning to the others.

It was Mrs. Mingot. Rose noticed that a black wool shawl had been thrown over the girl's head, half covering her face. Suddenly she was fascinated by the spectacle. The four women took up the chorus again, with shaky voices.

"By Thy Precious Blood, have mercy on Thy faithful trespassers.

"Poor sinners we are, beseeching Thy Mercy."

"Thy Mercy!" shouted Mrs. Mingot, trying to cover the stammering of the others.

"Thy Mer-cy!" declaimed Mrs. Mingot.

"Close your eyes," Rose told herself, suddenly overcome by an unknown disturbance.

"We beseech Thee therefore that Thy Judicial Sentence weigh not heavily upon her," chanted the unrelenting voices.

"Together! Together!" ordered someone.

"Aren't they ever going to finish?" thought Rose, struggling to keep her eyes closed.

"We beseech Thee therefore that Thy Judicial Sentence weigh not heavily upon her!" chanted the voices, suddenly joined by many others. "That Thy Judicial Sentence weigh not heavily upon her!" The clamor increased.

"You must open your eyes," Rose told herself. A hand was touching her shoulder, shaking her. She found herself standing behind the woman who had roused her from her feigned nap. "Do Thou conduct her to a place of peace and rest!"

All the women, some standing, some kneeling on the tiles, turned toward the seated girl whose face was now completely covered by the black veil.

"Together!" someone shouted again.

The noise swelled like a coming storm.

"Do Thou, O Lord, rescue this soul from the flame and may the angels lead her to the land of the living," the women repeated after Mrs. Mingot. "To the land of the living. Lamb of God Who takest away the sins of the world, grant her eternal peace. Eternal peace!" the women repeated in chorus. Some were crying; one could hear tears under their voices; others, on their knees, were clutching the benches, their heads bent back.

"Lamb of God," implored a voice a little further away and carried over by the resonance of the room, "grant her eternal peace!"

"What if he is dead?" Rose thought all of a sudden.

Her hands began to tremble, her whole body trembled. "No, that's impossible! Lamb of God, deliver me from this thought! Lamb of God!" she was going to shout herself when, suddenly, everything fell silent. The prayer was probably over, it had always been like that in her life. . . .

Mrs. Mingot found Rose prostrate on the bench and thought that she was sleeping. Attracted by the noise nurses paced up and down the room, doing surprise about-faces with angry looks. They had taken the shawl off the girl's head. She continued to stare straight ahead, without moving.

"No matter what they do, she's had the last rites," said Mrs. Mingot.

Her face glowed with contentment and she looked with tenderness at Rose who had just opened her eyes.

"I've had a ghastly thought," murmured Rose, "something like a revelation. But it's not true! It can't be true!" she cried, shaking her head, plunging her face into her hands.

"Then why talk about it, if it isn't true?" replied Mrs. Mingot. "These truths are quite enough for the time being," she added, pointing to the girl for whom she had prayed. She sighed. "Ah, I don't like to see death come back among us. You'll see: one death always brings another. This one will start a whole series. . . . A year or so ago, it began with Lydia, a Czech. For several days we had all noticed that she was growing taller. Not much, just enough for me to know what it was all about: death often announces itself like that. Days passed; it was in the month of March, if I remember correctly, there were daffodils in the garden: I detest daffodils. One night Lydia went up to bed, straight as an 'I.' She had the bed at my right. Suddenly, in the middle of the night, I saw her pale white hand flutter like a bird's wing. I yelled: 'The dove! The dove!' Everybody thought I was dreaming. At that time everybody yelled at night in the dormitory. Not like now. We put up a good fight . . . well, anyhow, the next morning Lydia was dead, dead. . . . Let me finish!" shouted Mrs. Mingot who thought that Rose, who had begun to fidget, wanted to interrupt her.

"Dead?" said Rose pensively.

Without hearing her, her friend went right on.

"After Lydia, two other women died in the same fashion. Lydia had thrown them the line on her way out. . . . Why did they die? Why? For the salvation of their country, for the revolution? To protest to the face of heaven? To redeem our sins? Yes, perhaps for this, perhaps for that. Yes, perhaps for this and for that together. But dead all the same, Rose! Dead, I tell you!

"No cause, no salvation stands up to this total blackness.

Death denies everything. Every night I could argue that day never existed: the sky would prove me right. Death is really the worst catastrophe: everything collapses with you. Love never existed; light never existed. Everything negated in an instant. All those crumpled images, those feelings, every second of life, the sun: I used to exist. Nothing replaces existence. They were as dead as a handful of pebbles, condemned by death, betrayed by death, they were wearing the stone hat, Rose, the stone hat!"

She buried her face in her hands and Rose respected her silence. "Why is she telling me all this? Does she know something?"

"What about him, do you think he is dead?" she finally asked the old woman in a trembling voice.

Mrs. Mingot looked up. Her face was dry, her eyes were calm.

"But this has nothing to do with him, Rose, why should this have anything to do with him? I am only thinking of us, we're the only ones who count now. You are here, you are with us, my dear! Warm and cuddly and for a good long time. Leave that man in peace, he is resting far, far away, a little farther every day. You are no longer his life. You are no longer in his life. He is no longer in yours. Isn't everything just right that way? Only one thing: not to die, no, not to die just yet. . . ."

Nervously she clutched at Rose's hand as though, in saying these words, she were facing a danger. Rose pulled her hand away sharply.

"What does death matter to me, if he is dead, or if I am never to see him again!" she cried.

Mrs. Mingot shrugged and got up. Some of the women were gathering again at the other end of the room where the girl for whom they had prayed was sitting. Mrs. Mingot went over to find out how things stood. Rose was escaping her a little more every day. She had to do something to console herself.

The old woman's words had not frightened Rose. She did not believe in these fables, but that such superstitions (Paul's intentional staying away, his indifference) were at all possible, threw her into a kind of fit. So they had come to think, around here, that from the depth of his silence Paul approved of the punishment that was being inflicted upon her, that he was trying to make it even harder. What nonsense! Still, for over two months she had been almost entirely sane again, lucid, yet she was still as locked up, as abandoned as on the first day. The doctor who had, one day, talked of hell in front of her, often walked through Section Two: "Rose Schmidt, you'll be angry with me again!" he exclaimed as soon as he saw her. "I still have not received any information concerning your husband. No, you needn't tell me that I should write, I have already written several times. But we ought to have a little chat, one of these days, you and I. But not just yet, my dear, not just yet. I'm much too busy. And besides, we still have a little more progress to make before we are completely well again. Come now, it's not so bad here, is it: the food has been much, much better during the last month, hasn't it? And the room is nice and warm now. If all goes well, I'll have some raffia brought in in a couple of days. Did you hear that, little Mother Lormot? And you, Redempcion, listen to this: next week I'll have bundles of raffia and cane brought in here, and a few tools which we'll entrust to the most reasonable, and a few pots of paint as well. To begin we'll have someone teach you how to braid baskets and sandals and sun hats. . . ."

"Sun hats!" exclaimed Mother Lormot with a shrug, pointing to the window. The sky was low. Fog drifted in the black branches. As a consolation one could always tell oneself that it was going to snow. But sun hats! There would never be any sun again. Two months ago it had rolled behind the trees like a severed head and no one had spoken of it since.

"But these hats won't be for you," replied the man. "We'll sell them. It will bring in money for you all."

"Could we braid them in different designs in different colors?" asked Gertrude.

"Certainly!" cried the stout man with enthusiasm. "We're not opposed to imagination. I just told you, I'll bring you paints. Those with a feeling for art can create to their heart's content."

"Perhaps we could also make little mats," timidly suggested a young girl at Big Mama Houdin's arm. She had ribbons in her hair like a schoolgirl.

"A good idea; a splendid idea!" cried the man. "Little mats to place under a plate, or for serving tea. Oh, I can see that you have lots of ideas. I'll soon have a workshop buzzing with champion straw weavers. . . . Only Rose Schmidt isn't saying anything. . . ."

"She is thinking about her husband," said Mrs. Mingot flatly. "Why don't you tell her the truth? She is strong enough to take it. And besides, I'm here. At least let her hate him, once and for all!"

The stout man flushed purple. "It's none of your business!" he screamed. "I wasn't talking to you! Mrs. Mingot, I'm fully aware that you never miss an opportunity to talk all kinds of rubbish, always trying to make things worse, and your condition has nothing to do with it. I know you, and I give you one last warning: change your behavior, or else. . . ."

Mrs. Mingot showed the first signs of panic which she always felt when she was directly confronted, but this time the affront was in public, and her pride carried her away. "Change my behavior?" she asked with feigned surprise. "Annette, go and fetch me another behavior, please," she said, lifting the hem of her asylum dress between two fingers and pointing at it with her chin.

Several women burst out laughing. The stout man stared at her with blazing eyes. "And you over there, with nothing to do but fold your arms," pursued Mrs. Mingot, encouraged by her success, "didn't you hear: I absolutely must, I have been commanded, to change 'behavior,' and I need space for my further evolutions. These walls are much too close together. Knock them down for me, will you! Or else our dear director will have a fit. . . ."

"Mrs. Mingot, that's enough of your act!" shouted the stout man, taking a step toward the old woman. "Get out of here! Go into the yard, that's an order! Mrs. Lemercier!" he called, turning about.

Alerted by the loud voices, the nurse came running at once. The scene had excited the women. They were drifting into disorder. They snickered at Mrs. Mingot's last words, they laughed and forgot to stop laughing; there was something mechanical, suddenly painful in their throats. "Hand over your keys then, if you want me to go out!" shrieked Mrs. Mingot, now completely out of control. "We don't get to see your keys very often, Mr. Behavior Changer, they're always snuggling in your pocket, those darling keys! We can wait a thousand years at the bottom of our hole if your sweet little keys say NO!"

"Bravo!" cried Redempcion, "next week we'll braid him a raffia key ring!" The nurse did not dare take on Mrs. Mingot; she jerked Redempcion by the arm and roughly dragged her toward the door. Somewhere a woman began to sob.

"Martha, don't sob like that!" said a woman. "Stop sobbing, Martha."

Mrs. Mingot had vanished. The women finally stopped laughing.

The stout man mopped his forehead. "Calm down, ladies," he said, "please calm down!" He did not realize they were already quiet again. "Let's forget this regrettable incident and the eccentricities of that poor woman. I shall bring you the raffia as I promised. You are too inactive. We must become a community with occupations and interests. Your health depends on it . . . and so does mine. This is our home, at least for the time being, the asylum is our world."

He was talking to himself. He noticed it probably, because he stopped and walked to the door with slightly stooped shoulders. Rose watched him go. Around her, the hubbub started up again. "Why did I laugh so hard, a minute ago, at what Mrs. Mingot said?" she asked herself.

And then, suddenly, she realized that during those few minutes she had stopped thinking of Paul and that, that really was hell. . . .

"I agree with you about it being hell," said Mrs. Mingot.

Rose wondered if she had been thinking out loud.

"But you have just seen how their creation can turn against them. Do you want me to tell you something? They don't rule us any longer. They've come too late with their kind words and their bundles of straw. Too late. Anarchy is loose, a fire they can't put out now. If they want to get their power back, they'll have to kill us one by one. And I'll be the first to go, I'm fully aware of that!"

A sigh swelled her narrow chest. "Let's go. It's time for supper."

Once more the community rites absorbed their attention. Outside, night had fallen.

The evening meal always brought a sort of peace to the women. With calmed faces they sat around the metal tables, in the yellowish light of the ceiling lamps. Hurriedly they emptied their aluminum bowls so that they could have them refilled before the pots were taken away. Suddenly there were fewer crises, fewer lapses.

A full soup spoon dropped noisily on the rim of a bowl, from a distracted hand before it reached the mouth, a piece of bread, thrown at an imaginary animal under the table, a mug of water intentionally spilled on the metal table top—all these passed like meteors across the family atmosphere of the meal. The dinner table was a sort of plateau on which almost all the fires of insanity burned out. At table the slightest incongruity seemed to be the beginning of still another madness, much worse and open to unanimous disapproval. Of course this lull did not always extend to the conversations.

"Hey, this may be her last meal!" cried Roubillot.

She pointed her finger at the new woman whose fate had been revealed by the cards. Big Mama Houdin shrugged and went on eating. She did not like to bother with the supernatural unless the cards had been spread out, and especially not at mealtime. But Redempcion who was sitting next to Big Mama Houdin kept nudging her with her elbow.

"Say yes, say yes! And watch her fold up!"

"Redempcion!" cried Mrs. Mingot, "just a little while ago you were praying for her salvation and now you want her to fold up! Who is being fooled here? Am I to assume that you were trying to deceive me and that what you were holding out to her with all that fake fervor was something like bloody wafer? Think back now, think back!"

"When I think back, all I can remember is a monkey's ass that looked like your face," cried Redempcion.

"Redempcion!" cried Mrs. Mingot, "take that back at once! I curse you, there, I curse you!"

"For God's sake, be quiet," said Rose, pulling at Mrs. Mingot's sleeve.

The wave of pity that had threatened to flood her entire heart a moment ago was gone. "This is your new family. Go ahead and love them."

"Aren't you eating any more?" asked Mrs. Mingot. "I can see you're all worked up. Did you find a pebble in the lentils? Or maybe you're still thinking about your husband, and that, too, must be hard to chew. . . ."

She had raised her voice for the others to hear. She was trying for a comeback after Redempcion's insult; and besides, her friendship with Rose was over, she spat on it, she spat on all friendships. Ah, they didn't know a thing about her! They didn't know what it meant to be a rebel!

"But he's just a blotter, that husband of yours!" she continued with a strange laugh. "What a lot of tears he needs! So many tears, and you're certainly not stingy. . . ."

Rose said nothing. "A living husband," she repeated to herself, "a living husband. . . ."

A living husband, a perfect husband, a unique husband.

Long before endowing him, as now, with all the virtues of resurrection, Rose had been conscious of how perfectly he fitted into each one of her molds. Even his appearance seemed to be making an effort: not too tall; not too short; not too handsome; not too ugly. And it was the same for his moral virtues. The system proceeded by absences, by default. A living husband, a perfect husband, a unique husband meant a pruned-down husband. "How cruel I am," thought Rose, wiping her eyes with her sheet.

Subjecting him like this to the despotism of analysis made her cry faster than anything else. Her love was her tears. In her mind she willfully mistreated the beloved image, shot cruel darts at the soft target, arrows of lucidity superior to love, dismissed the image, made it disappear, brought it back with an impudent jolt: she discovered the rite of sacrilege.

Drunk to tears with blasphemy, after evoking a reality that left her exhausted, unable to move, with eyes burning and her heart open, there remained his name, this word, this syllable "Paul."

Like a family of invisible pet birds, dozens of first names lived within the asylum walls. Last names had not followed them. Flown from the nests of distant birth certificates, the first names led, in this place where they had taken refuge, the hasty, naïve life of souls who have left their bodies.

Big Mama Houdin often spoke of Gabriel—her son, her

brother, her husband, no one knew. Julia Vuillaume sometimes spoke of Bertha; an old white-haired woman talked of Louis. Through her tears Martha called for a Martha who was not herself, or else what was one to think? Among these fluttered, less frequently, like migratory birds intercepted on a long-distance flight or creations from some faraway sunny island, Charleses, Octavians, Luciens, Albertas, Peters and Bertrands, some croaking nostalgically, others chirping meekly into the night of oblivion which was falling all around them, or else soon exhausted, silenced by the brief, deceptive splendor of a dawn. Among them Paul, flying steadily, untiringly.

The first time he had flown, with a dull flapping of nocturnal wings as though still blind, and frightened by the closeness of these unknown walls, it had been in that hotel by the sea where, from the ordinary vacation Rose had come to spend, she had begun slipping into another kind of vacation with wider, more lavish horizons: a vacation from her sanity.

Since then, what flights, what metamorphoses! Sometimes she strode through life with a falcon on her fist, her eyes looking straight ahead, closing the whole world into her hunting preserve; at other times, during the brief carnal moments of love, she had watched a macaw unfold his wide wings, like a stiff, quivering, multi-colored fan; with closed claws he leaned backwards, never letting go of his perch bar; sometimes she had followed the circlings of a hawk with eyes slitted from too much sun; sometimes she had listened to the satiated sleep of a dove. . . .

"It's been said that Rose Schmidt will always be the last one to go downstairs!" exclaimed a nurse, holding open the dormitory door and impatiently jangling her keys.

Rose was stuffing objects into a little bag that Mrs. Mingot had made for her out of an old black satin lining, at the time of their friendship; things acquired at the price of endless patience, sometimes due to the blind, chaotic generosity of those women for whom the hour of giving had struck (when, a moment later, the hour of taking back struck, they stood in the middle of the room, motionless and dispossessed, their memory suddenly empty), things one found in the courtyard or in the washrooms, things which no longer belonged to anyone.

A comb with a few teeth missing, an empty match box for needles, or stamps, a sharp-edged scrap of mirror (nothing has such pointed angles, such curves, as a broken mirror), a red cardboard wallet that leaves suspicious traces on the moist towel one has taken along, an empty tin box, still powdery inside from the sugar coating of cough drops, an old, torn book, chapters five and six of a story that takes place in Scotland, those were the things put to anonymous use, things on which ownership left no mark. By losing them, by giving them at random to the first woman one met (in the hour of giving that always struck at a moment of loneliness and just after one had cried), one returned them to a collective need which reached everywhere and which washed them of the marks and memories of possession.

By their very anonymity these objects became a kind of incongruous currency. Still, the desire for ownership was strong enough so that each woman felt the urge to drag around a cloth pocket dangling from a finger by a string that one wound and unwound incessantly.

"Rose Schmidt, how much longer are you going to stuff junk into that bag?"

Rose hurried to the door with a feeling that she had forgotten something. Just in case, she passed her hand through her hair while the nurse slammed the dormitory door behind her. Rose ran down the stone steps, her little black cloth bag bouncing against her legs. She had returned to her simplicity. True, the memory of Paul hardly ever left her, but neither did the little black cloth bag, this bag filled with miserable essentials. Finally she reached the big room, where winter (perhaps only a spring that resembled winter) continued to keep the women indoors. For a moment surprise held her nailed to the threshold. She had pushed the door open and hesitated to close it behind her.

Disregarding all proportions, it was like a living tree, a monkey arbor, a human-sized ant heap. During the first seconds, life, movement denied all identity, all singling out, because the milling about of the women untiringly substituted one face for another. The voices copied each other, fused into one another, answered a question with a similar question, mingled with echoes, questioned questions, answered answers. A woman who had just called out in one direction suddenly ran off in another, while a different woman appeared in her place, her mouth open from a cry she had not uttered, offered to an absurd fate.

Some women remained glued to the wall like blue stains, then came running up, suddenly voluminous, heavy with a kind of excessive presence, then turned abruptly as though snatched up in the sliding of a convex mirror. There never seemed to be a moment of rest within the sweaty walls, which steamed as though they contained a furiously boiling stew.

Rose stepped into the room and everything around her seemed to calm down. Roubillot passed and winked maliciously, followed by three little girls, round-eyed and intent like small fish swimming after the larger one. Mrs. Mingot came up to Rose.

"I'm not talking to you any more! For two days you have constantly pretended not to know me. I've become too disreputable, uh? Well, let me tell you, you haven't heard the last of me!"

Rose was going to protest, but the old woman had already disappeared. The confusion had started again all around her, the threads that snored around the shuttle, the madness, the roar of the looms. She brushed her hand over her forehead. She, too, was going to join the dance, she, too, was going to set to work, she was going to spin again. . . .

During a whole period of that winter (or of that spring that so much resembled winter) Rose turned in circles. She started in the morning, as soon as she came down from the dormitory. She thought that it would be on a day like this that Paul would come. About ten o'clock she allowed herself a break and went to sit on a bench, near the other women, silent as she, attentive to the signs of their illness. By that time Rose had walked around the room at least a hundred times. With her eyes she measured the surface of the area; in her mind she estimated the job still to be done, with the calm determination of workmen sitting on the scaffolding during their lunch hour.

The success of each turn around the room depended on two conditions: the first was of a strictly technical nature. Each time you tried to walk the greatest possible distance, hugging the walls and keeping the same pace. This required that none of the other women who were wandering about the room come over to block your path. The corners of the room with the change of direction they required punctuated the walk rather pleasantly. If no one got in your way or blocked the corner, obliging you to take a short cut or a detour, you turned with perfect regularity, you became the wife of time.

The second condition for success was more difficult to define. But it was good, at any rate, to take the date of whatever day it was, for a starting point (no one knew the date; one had to ask a nurse who often answered with anything that came into her head) or simply take the seasons: winter, spring, summer, autumn, and then go backwards from one year to the next.

Rain, if it happened to be raining outside, could also serve as a pretext and call up memories of other rainy days. But there are all sorts of rains: first of all there is summer rain and winter rain; there are a lot of subtle differences in the rustling, the light, the odor of each rain.

Rarer, snow was also more reliable: memories inscribed themselves black on white. Thus, the wind, the date: February twenty-third, night falling at five o'clock, could every day suggest a subject for meditations, retrieve from the bottom of memory a less lonely season with a lighter sky than the one outside.

But in the afternoon, or toward evening, suddenly the thought —like a cry, suppressed all day: "When will I see him again? Will I ever see him again?" The lamps had been lit. Shadows were ambling across the floor, naked reefs, hurdles, black outlines inviting one to fail. Rose sat down on the bench, stretched her tired legs and rediscovered her companions, as fresh as in the first hour, animated by the nervousness of night.

Sometimes she searched through the crowd for Mrs. Mingot. She was not at all surprised at the radical change in behavior that made the old woman seek out the loudest and most rebellious women in the section. Such metamorphoses were common here. Freedom fermenting inside, the calls, the temptations of freedom, blood kicking in the veins could throw one very fast into far greater excesses than insanity.

For the last couple of days Mrs. Mingot had been letting go with a violence of which Rose had not thought her capable. She hardly ever left the gang formed by Redempcion, Gertrude, Roubillot and one or two of her disciples, with Big Mama Houdin sitting close by like a sleeping sage, an asthmatic advisor. For a long time Mrs. Mingot had been considered an arrogant woman with a weakness for denunciations. Only thanks to her scene with the director had she been admitted into the circle which, moreover, at the slightest provocation—and often as a game—broke up and regrouped itself far from her, at the other end of the room a moment after she had been admitted. At those moments Rose could see Mrs. Mingot rapidly crossing the room, trying hard to hide her confusion under a grimace of fiendish joy, an air of "trouble shooting," a painful exaggeration of the subversive sentiments that were to allow her reintegration into the mocking, evasive circle.

Sometimes Rose was tempted to go up to her former companion. Hadn't Mrs. Mingot plunged into these excesses because of her disappointment in friendship? "I talked too much about Paul. I locked myself into my memories. She came to me on the first day, she guided me, offered me her chatty, cordial presence, her relentless, ardent friendship at a time when everything was slipping. As soon as I was able to come back to life, to my life, find my past again, I turned away from her," Rose told herself. But she didn't budge. It was too late.

Even if it was through disappointment and bitterness, Mrs. Mingot had found a form of new life, a new fate. She who had always talked of hell was now pushing it to extremes. She was fanning the flames of her truth. One night she tried to set fire to the asylum.

Patiently she had stuffed her little sack full of bits of paper, rags soaked with grease and oil during meals, twigs she had picked up in the yard. No one ever found out how she was able to get hold of matches.

She had slipped out of the room and sneaked into a linen closet on the second floor where sheets lay folded on wooden shelves. When she reappeared, she winked to the women of the gang who were awaiting her return in a state of excitement occasionally heightened by gestures of panic. The secret had been let out long before she came back. The whispering brought the news to Rose who was stopping from her rounds. "Mingot—" since her plunge into insubordination she was hardly ever called "Mrs." any more—"Mingot has just set fire to the linen closet." Why the linen closet, wondered Rose.

"Good work! They drive us crazy with their linen!" said a women near her.

"But we'll be burned alive!" screamed another woman, jumping up. "We're locked in!"

She rushed to the door. Others followed.

"Fire! Fire!" they began to screech.

Through the glass door of the room they could see smoke coming down the staircase. Nurses were running in all directions. Everywhere alarm bells started ringing. The screams of the women were deafening. At last the doors to the courtyard were opened. The women ran out onto the soggy lawn. Night was falling. Calls answered each other throughout the gardens, under the trees, dragged out beyond the walls. The director drove up in a car, with men in black. The brakes screeched to a stop on the gravel. Somewhere, a church bell was ringing. No flames were visible.

In the darkness Rose looked for Mrs. Mingot. She found her in the center of a group of women, pale, speechless. She was replying to the questions they were asking her with a mere nod of the head, trying to smile like an exhausted champion on the verge of collapse who is being congratulated for his victory.

"Leave her alone," Rose said to the women.

She took Mrs. Mingot's arm and pulled her toward the end of the courtyard. The firemen arrived, and the women gathered around the engine. Walking closely along the asylum walls, Rose and Mrs. Mingot reached a deserted spot. Rose recognized it as the place where, so many times at the beginning of her internment, she had sat with Mrs. Mingot.

"Do you remember?" said Mrs. Mingot who also recognized the spot and came out of her silence with a slightly weary voice. "How hot it was then! When was it? A year ago? Two years ago?"

"Eight months," said Rose.

"Ah, you were all wedged into yourself at that time," pursued Mrs. Mingot. "The first days you never opened your mouth. And eyes as big as saucers. Saucers full of water, because you were crying. You've always cried a lot here."

"I cry much less now," said Rose, her throat taut.

"God, how hot it was! Sometimes I'd say to you: Come, Rose, let's sit in the shade, or you'll be ready for Section Three. . . ."

"Yes," said Rose.

"And now it is I who am ready for Section Three," pursued Mrs. Mingot, hanging her head. "You won't see me again, Rose, never again. No one here will see me again. One day you'll hear that I died, and I'll have been dead for a long time. They don't keep you informed here," she added in an articulated voice, no longer her own.

"Mrs. Mingot . . ." stammered Rose.

"Never mind, Rose, don't say anything," murmured Mrs. Mingot, lifting a shaking hand. Her voice was about to break. She got hold of herself again. "Yes, how you used to cry! And Paul? Where do you stand with him now?"

Policemen had come into the yard. They took big steps, walking one behind the other.

"Sometimes I have the feeling that he'll come any moment," answered Rose. "He'll take me away with him at once. You know, we are such a perfectly united couple. It makes people smile, they don't believe such fidelity exists, such a unique love. And yet you only have to see him, see him look at me, to understand. His eyes become all golden. One always thinks that I am boasting. But it's really true; besides, his love, this almost excessive love, I admit, I return it completely: he is my life. Sometimes, I think he must be dead or he would have come. But that's impossible. I would have known; something, at that very moment, would have snapped inside me. . . ."

"Don't worry," said Mrs. Mingot, "he is not dead . . . and he still loves you. I can tell you now: I don't feel him dead. My own death, yes. But what do we matter, you and I! Life is all outside of us. We must put an end to this hell, Rose! Life means the others. . . . Rose, Rose!" she cried very quickly, "here we are, you and I, against the wall. How hot it was! I used to tell you my stories. . . . No, no don't cry! Don't cry, Rose, please don't cry, do you remember, that's from the opera 'The Dragoons of Villars.' Rose. . . ."

The fire had already been put out. The firemen were rolling up their hoses, talking loudly into the night. The policemen filed out through the gates. Nurses were calling the roll, shouting the women's names, rushing about everywhere in the thickening darkness.

"Don't cry, Rose," Mrs. Mingot said again.

Men were coming toward them, led by the director.

"Sorry, Mrs. Mingot, you'll have to come with us," he said softly.

The old woman bent down and tore a small dead leaf from a bush, blackened with frost. Two male nurses in white smocks had seized her without harshness, each taking an arm. Mrs. Mingot raised her hand, the little dead leaf trembling between her fingers. Already they were taking her away.

"Look, Rose, Rose!" she cried, "do you remember: it's freezing. . . ."

A voice from the distance, slightly theatrical, slightly broken. They led Rose back into the flooded dining hall where, this evening, the women sat quietly.

And life went on within the high asylum walls. The summer (perhaps only a spring that resembled summer) came again, and the leaves. Again they went out into the courtyard, white-washed with sun. Stimulated by the fire, by the damage it had done, and especially by those flames that seemed ready to soar up again at any moment and whose existence the fire had revealed, the director undertook what he called a reorganization of the services. They finally did receive raffia and straw.

Rose was chosen to direct the workshop which, in good weather, was set up under the trees, with women singing in off-key voices. They braided little mats, baskets, sandals, sun hats. The director took a great interest in the work and spent long moments sitting beside Rose, smoking a cigar.

"Rose Schmidt," he began, "I always tell you that we ought to have a little chat, just you and I. And then, when I sit here beside you, as at this moment, with a few minutes to spare, I don't feel like talking about you and your past any more. I look at you: you are calm, perfectly lucid, a bit dreamy perhaps. I say to myself: but she knows, she remembers. But in your presence, Rose Schmidt, I begin to believe that conscience and memory exist only when one accepts them. And perhaps reality only exists when one wants it.

"I also tell myself that one invents less in lies and dreams than in a confession. Yes, all those things, all that you represent behind your smiling, closed face, is very disturbing, Rose Schmidt, very disturbing. And I prefer to see you here, living in your false hopes, than dying somewhere else of real despair. Above all I bet on life, and against reason. I take part in your game. The seasons take part in it, too: you live. But I talk and talk and you don't answer, and you're right not to answer. Your reason is stronger than mine. You alone, after all, know how to deny. That is a great virtue. Very rare. Your love exists in spite of everything, Rose Schmidt, and I am happy to be its helper. . . ."

He got up, put his hand on Rose's shoulder and walked off under the trees.

"Red, three strands, Annette," said Rose. "No, not raspberry red. Cherry red. Thank you. Two green. . . . Straw now, a whole handful while you're at it: that's for the bottom. . . ."

The silence of the summer afternoon settled down, hardly troubled by the women's talk: "The handles, Redempcion, we're waiting!" "Oh, you old needle thief, you devil, you!"

Insanity was still there, under the asylum trees, but so was summer, so was hope.

"Six blue, please, Annette," said Rose. "No, change this one. Look, it's badly dyed. . . ."

She wiped a few drops of sweat from her forehead with the

back of her hand, looked at the light-flooded sky. The images of life were there: this talky community, easily delirious, in the midst of which Rose was establishing her power a little more each day; her authority grew, those humble daily tasks, the play of blue strands, and red, and yellow, and green, in which insanity was gradually trapping itself, the past forgiven, summer in the leaves. Rose was dreaming, with idle hands, her eyes far away. It was good not to know just yet, not yet to want to remember.

Vocation D'Être Heureux

by MARC ALYN

Je voudrais être heureux une fois dans ma vie
N'avoir plus peur de l'ombre ni des hommes
Ne plus craindre les murs enfermant mon corps
Etre celui qui va insouciant des heures
Se mêler à l'espoir des feuilles

Ne plus craindre que mon coeur
Cesse soudain de me parler à l'oreille
Que la chaîne de mon sang
Se brise net dans mes doigts

Connaîre le printemps
Et sa douceur de barque à la dérive
Regarder le ciel dans les yeux
Mêler nos corps dans les blés murs

Seulement être libre
Une heure dans ma vie
Une heure qui résonnerait longtemps
Comme un cristal choqué en moi
Avant de se briser sur la barrière du temps

Je voudrais aller au fond de mon amour
Dans ce couloir humide dont les parois s'effritent à mon passage
Presser mes désirs jusqu'à l'écorce
Etre heureux c'est peut-être aussi
Choisir la douleur qui vous plaît.

English Translation

by D'ELBERT E. KEENAN

I should like to be happy one time in my life
To feel no terror of the shades or men
To fear no more the walls that pen my flesh
To be one who walks heedless of the hours
To merge with the hopefulness of leaves

To fear no longer lest my heart
Cease suddenly to whisper in my ear
Lest the linked chain of my blood
Snap clean in my fingers' grasp

To know the springtide
And its sweetness like a boat adrift
To look heaven straight in the eyes
To merge our bodies in the ripened wheat

Merely to be free
For one hour of my life
One hour which would ring out lengthily
Like a crystal struck within myself
Before it breaks against the barrier of time

I should like to go to my love's very depths
In this dank corridor whose walls crumble away as I pass
    through them
To squeeze my desires to the husk
To be happy, it may be, is also
To choose one's own happiness.

FROM Degrés, a novel*

by MICHEL BUTOR

Translated by URSULE MOLINARO
and VENABLE HERNDON

I was standing on the deck of the ship, leaning over the wooden
railing, watching Marseilles draw nearer, next to me Micheline
Pavin, a kerchief over her hair to protect it from the wind, de-
claring:

"What a shame we didn't meet a few days earlier in
Athens . . .";

you, at Etangs, with your brothers and your cousins, not
inside the house, of course not, not at that hour, it was such a
beautiful day, but in the tree house you were constructing in
the heart of the Herrecourt Woods,

your Uncle Henri sitting at his big black table before the
open window overlooking the garden with its few fruit trees
and beyond the little wall the fields already mown, the woods
and hills of Bresles;

but that wasn't what he was looking at, shifting his pipe
between his teeth, inhaling the smell of the leaves, with the air
coming in and moving the curtains,

he was looking at the presents he had been given at lunch for

* The complete text of this novel is to be published in the U.S. by Simon
and Schuster.

149

his thirty-ninth birthday: a tin of English tobacco, a blue-and-black tie, and a book on Italian painting,

which he put away two weeks later, two weeks ago, the window closed, this time, whipped by the torrential rain of a thunderstorm that had been in the air for two days,

in the fat leather suitcase set on the same black table amid the ashtrays and the magazines and which he left standing there, already full, and which he was able to close only with your help.

Your Aunt Rose:

"Henri, Denis, Pierre, hurry up! The car is already here."

I had been back in Paris for a long time that Tuesday; I was in my room with Micheline Pavin; I was showing her books, the few articles I had already published in various reviews . . . ;

and the following Monday, it was the first day of the new term; we found ourselves in the classroom, both of us, you and I, no longer uncle and nephew, but student and teacher; I was seeing a good many of your classmates for the first time, and therefore, before beginning our geography lesson, I circulated a white sheet of paper among you, on which I asked you to write your name, your address, the date of your birth, and your parents' profession into the rectangle corresponding to the seat you occupied;

your Uncle Henri was doing the same with his twelfth-graders, modern course; then he told them what their schedule of studies was going to be:

"Mondays and Tuesdays: eighteenth- and nineteenth-century literature, Wednesdays: plays, first *Iphigénie* by Racine, then *Tartuffe,* and finally *Cinna,* Fridays: Greek and Latin authors in translation, composition once a month, handed in on Tuesday, returned the following Tuesday,"

and was trying to impress them with a healthy fear of the finals, with a healthy awareness of the rapid passage of time, of the fact that the final test was only a small number of weeks away, a speech completely parallel to the one he made you the following day,

because, although you had already had several lessons together, two in Latin and two in Greek (so that it was no longer necessary to circulate the questionnaire-seating plan),

due to one of those misunderstandings that are unavoidable in the excitement of the new term, the French course he is going to give you from now on every Monday from eleven to twelve had not yet been marked in that particular box of his schedule and, unaware of his duty, he had not been able to fulfill it,

with the result that on Tuesday, October fifth, at two in the afternoon you were having your first French class:

"Sixteenth- and seventeenth-century literature, on Mondays, Tuesdays and Fridays; the classical theatre on Wednesdays, first *Britannicus,* then *L'Ecole des femmes* and finally *Polyeucte;* homework handed in on Tuesday, for French as for everything else; one week French, one week Latin, one week Greek, that's not hard to remember, returned the following Tuesday, no extension granted; those who fail to hand in their work on time receive a zero; and to get right at it, open your composition books and mark down the following subject for next week's homework:

"Describe the day of your vacation that stands out most clearly in your memory; try to explain why this particular day seemed most memorable to you,"

with the usual warnings:

"Now let's understand each other; if everybody follows the rules, we'll get along fine,"

and naturally the little bell of the final exams already hung around your necks:

"Don't forget that the exams come at the end of the next year, and that it is impossible to do well in the twelfth grade if you've done poorly in the eleventh."

You couldn't get over the tremendous transformation that

was taking place before your eyes; that this kind man, so fanci-
ful, so full of games, whom you knew so well since he was your
Uncle Henri and you had just spent a month's vacation in his
house at Etangs, eating all your meals with him,

should be another all of a sudden, hard, harsh, slightly
sarcastic, never looking at you, as though he were trying to
avoid seeing you, as though you embarrassed him a little,

and you felt that there was a slight fear in him before all of
you, and especially before you;

you felt that it was within your power to make life extremely
difficult for him,

that you might exploit this unusual situation, in order to
acquire a certain prestige in the eyes of your classmates, by
cleverly heckling this relative of yours, and that this would
doubtlessly have unpleasant consequences for you at home, that
your Uncle Henri could obviously complain about you to your
father or to your mother and cause you all kinds of unpleasant-
ness from that direction, but that he would be more or less de-
fenseless inside the classroom;

at this point you became conscious of a feeling toward him
that was, for you, totally unexpected, that was somehow in
contradiction to all your previous experiences with him, notably
to your relationship of the preceding month at Etangs,

a slight feeling of pity, and this seemed so fantastic to you
that you blushed violently, you passed your hands over your
face, trembling a little.

He noticed your confusion and for a split second a bit of his
smile from down there returned.

I was getting acquainted with my little sixth-graders: they
would have to keep a notebook now, take notes; it would not be
difficult at first, I was going to dictate to them slowly what they
were to write down, but after a while I would only dictate chapter titles and section headings, they would have to make their
own choice of the things I would say; and I would check the

notebooks very often, at each question period they would be given marks for their notebooks, which would be as important as the marks for their answers. They would have to keep them neatly and illustrate them intelligently with pictures cut out of old books or with postcards that they would try to dig up;

after my first lesson with them: history and pre-history, I climbed the stairs in the corner of the courtyard, I passed the classrooms of the tenth- and eleventh-graders just as the doors were being opened and the students came out to breathe and stretch a bit, I nodded to my old and new colleagues who were changing rooms and audiences, I came here:

"Who can give me a definition of the Middle Ages?"

Silence, of course, then, slightly hesitant, three hands went up. I picked the one closest to me, just in front of you, near the window, in the first row. I did not know his name yet; he didn't know whether to stand up or stay seated.

"Well? What are you waiting for?"

I waved my fingers to encourage him to speak; he interpreted it as an order to stand up.

"What's your name?"

"Alain Mouron."

"Where were you last year?"

"In Bourges."

"Now there's a town where one should know all about the Middle Ages. Well?"

"It is the period between the fall of the Roman Empire and the Renaissance."

(His Uncle Bailly, for the first time with his "philosophers," was trying to speak to them in English, to make them speak in English, perfectly aware that it would not work, that in a few weeks he would no longer be able to make them utter any English words except those they read.)

"Very good. Be seated."

Michel Daval leaned over to you and whispered:

"That's my cousin."

You did not want to provoke a reprimand from me, especially not during the first days, but you were dying to pursue a little further this new conversation, this first establishment of contact, you began looking at your fountain pen as though you had suddenly discovered that it was not functioning properly, you plunged one arm into your bag and withdrew the list of textbooks recommended by your professors, and on it you scrawled, hastily, as though to test your recalcitrant pen:

"a first cousin?"

then, as though this test had reassured you of the good working condition of your instrument, you quickly crumpled up the paper and placed it on the window sill, a small, delicate white rock,

while your neighbor, his head very straight, his shoulders squared against the back of the bench, followed me with his eyes

(standing before the blackboard, I was asking:

"And who can tell me why this period is called the Middle Ages?"),

signaled you: no, with the left forefinger.

Only on Saturday did we see each other again in the classroom, for the next history lesson, because Wednesday's geography course doesn't take place every week, only once every two weeks, alternating with mathematics taught by Mr. du Marnet

(in his study, rue du Pré-aux-Clercs, under the low ceiling, your Uncle Henri was taking advantage of his day off to finish the preparation of a passage of the *Odyssey* with which he intended to start you reading Homer: Ulysses' arrival on Phaeacian shores; in front of him, the excerpts you are reading, Bailly's dictionary on the left, its purple linen binding veined by different-colored ink stains, some of them going back to the days when he himself was an eleventh-grader, fraying at the corners, exposing flaky gray cardboard,

Bérard's translation on the right, propped against the glass-brick ashtray in which he had forgotten his pipe, its delicate embers had burned out,

because these lines which he reread at the same period each year were charming him again, all kinds of ideas were waking up as they did each time, work projects that would fall asleep in the boredom of school routine; he dropped the strict program to take up Book V in its entirety);

you were looking at the double page of maps in your manual where all the great geographical discoveries of the Renaissance are shown, retracing Vasco da Gama's voyage to Calicut which you confused with Calcutta, Columbus' expeditions to the West Indies and, on the opposite page, the trip around the world of Magellan's crew, offering a circular no longer rectangular view of the planet, with the North Pole almost in the center, the continents unfolding all around it as though belted by this first periplus, as though to mark clearly the completely new importance, the completely new concrete aspect that the sphericity of the earth was gradually going to assume from that moment on, while up to then it had been a question of pure speculation;

then your eyes shifted to the dusty discarded globe on the corner of the empty wardrobe at the door, and you tried to imagine the waves, and the ships with their sails, evening descending on Philippine shores, which you peopled with palm trees,

listening distractedly across the billowing Pacific that was beginning to roar and across the surf between the islands to some of your classmates responding one after the other before the blackboard, which I obliged them to cover with crude and timid drawings of the Mediterranean or of America,

to my questions about the taking of Constantinople by the

Turks (it was our first question period), that of Granada by Isabella, the distribution of the newly discovered lands by the decision of the Borgia Pope Alexander VI,

before the lesson that day, Renaissance and Reformation.

The next day, in your Uncle Henri's study, buried deep in the leather armchair, my eyes just level with the table on which your Aunt Rose placed the coffee tray, beside the *Odyssey*, text and translation, opened at the beginning of Book VII, Entrance at the Palace of Alcinous,

I saw your Cousin Lucie through the half-open door across the hall, sitting on a small chair in her room, knitting a blue sweater for her doll.

A rain squall hit the windowpanes.

In the Verrières woods, with the Buffaloes, taking shelter in a tunnel, seated on the ground along the walls, looking at the muddy stream swelling between you,

at war, entrusted with an important assignment, to get through to headquarters with ultra-secret documents, plans for an atomic submarine, which the scattered enemy, the three other patrols, Mountain Goats, Tigers and Squirrels, were obviously trying to snatch away from you,

as yet unsure where exactly you were supposed to go, knowing only that an emissary whose description you had been given, would wait for you at the foot of a certain tall red beech five hundred yards south-east from your point of departure, and that he would hand over to you an envelope containing coded instructions and a topographical sketch,

you began to feel cold; the ground was becoming more and more damp, and besides it was getting late, already a quarter to three by your watch; you gave the starting signal; the red beech couldn't be much further now; first one of you to reconnoiter, then the others, stealthily, scanning the briers right and left, kerchiefs slipped through their belts, because loss of the kerchief stood for death in the game, you came last, your thumbs slipped under the shoulderstraps of your knapsack, softly whistling the melody of a scout song, beginning to find all this very silly.

Michel Daval was with his parents at the house of our colleague Bailly, rue Pierre-Leroux. He had been sent to the back room with the younger children who had, just this once, been given special permission to take out the electric train, a present from Grandfather and Grandmother Bailly (Pure madness, their mother had said, what an expense! And they don't even know how to play with it yet without getting it all out of order), which he had put up for them, for which he had constructed absolutely extraordinary bridges and signal posts with René's erector set, and with which he was letting them play on their own now, while he lay sprawled on one of the beds, leafing through the pile of magazines he had discovered on a shelf in the hall.

It was getting so dark, with the window looking out on a small triangular courtyard from the second floor of a six-storey building, they had to switch on the light.

At the other end of the apartment, in the working-living room with its two windows overlooking the street, with René and Elisabeth Bailly's two tables, with their two libraries, Mr. and Mrs. Daval were sitting in two deep Louis XVI armchairs upholstered in faded cretonne, at last asking the question they had not wanted to ask in the presence of the children:

"Well, and Elisabeth?"

He got up, nervous, lit a cigarette, forgetting to pass them around, glanced through one of the windows as though hoping to see a car drive up, then swung around,

"Well yes! She's gone to Orléans, to her family, last night, by car; she won't be back before tomorrow night; Monday is her day off, you know. She can't stand it any longer; she was practically in tears last Tuesday when she came home after her first day at the Lycée Aulnoy, and when I said to her: why didn't you ask for a leave of absence, she got mad; anything I say exasperates her these days. Well, I hope the week end will do her good."

In the Verrières woods, in the drizzle, clad in shorts and scout shirt, Alain Mouron, son of Henri Mouron first cousin of Mr. Bailly and Mrs. Daval, Alain Mouron of the Mountain Goat patrol sat squatting in the bushes with his comrades, waiting for you to pass with your Buffaloes, hoping to rob you of the famous plans; he sat quietly, careful not to move a branch; six or seven scouts came strolling by, chatted, made no effort whatsoever to hide themselves, passed right in front of him, but they belonged to another group; there was no need to fight them.

The following day, Monday, he came to sit next to you during drawing class, and questioned you in a low voice about this troop and its leaders, asking you if you'd been a scout for long, where you had camped last summer. Mr. Martin's approaching step made him stop; he pulled away a little, blinking; he drew a line in the middle of the face oval to indicate the position of the eyebrows.

The highlights of sun on Julius Caesar's plaster head had just disappeared; a whitish cloud passed above the glass case.

Mr. René Bailly told his twelfth-graders:

"*Macbeth* today; we continue with scene three, act one; you have it on page one hundred and seventy-six of your English Literature book; but it is absolutely essential that you get the complete tragedy, any edition will do, provided it doesn't give the translation on the facing page, obviously. Those who don't have it next Monday will be disciplined."

He struck the desk with his fist. His blond eyebrows contracted in a small fit of rage; he sat down, calmer, opened his hand finger by finger, placed it, flat, beside the open book, leafed through it, went a few pages further, stopped at the engraving of the three witches after Füssli, and came back.

"We are at Banquo's reply:
'What! can the devil speak true?'
which means? You tell us, Eller."
He was asking your brother Denis.
"Quoi, le démon peut parler vrai?"
Aha! But first of all it's a question. It should therefore be translated: *Quoi, le démon peut-il dire vrai?* Why does Banquo say this? Can you sum up for us what has happened?

The son of his cousin Daval, née Germaine Mouron, saw Julius Caesar's head in profile, but from the back, almost nose-less. His sheet of sketching paper was still completely white. He was absorbed in sharpening his pencil when Mr. Martin came up to him:

"Well, you haven't done anything yet?"
He looked at the pencil, took it, tried it.
"But my boy, this lead is much too hard! Don't you have charcoal? I'll give you a piece for now, but you must get into the habit of bringing your own materials; and your neighbor will let you borrow a bit of soft bread when you want to erase something."

Michel Daval took the charcoal, started to draw Caesar's ear, the cheek bone, the tip of the nose, the headband, extremely surprised by the result, by the total lack of resemblance between the grimacing face he had created, getting more and more horrible and sarcastic, and the *imperator's* plaster countenance at which he was looking, he stopped, no longer knowing what to do, waiting for the professor to come and put things right, then, as the professor was slow in coming, he borrowed a piece of soft bread from his neighbor Denis Regnier, in the same grade for the second year,

who, during the next lesson, while Mr. Hubert ran General Morin's machine in the amphitheatre before his elementary-math students to test the law of falling bodies,

in the eleventh-A classroom, instead of writing the subtitle:

"the hour" in his notebook as I told you to, merely checked to see if that was what he had written a year before, and began retracing his own name with a pencil point where he had cut it into the wood of his desk before he had fallen ill, six months ago.

Mr. Bonnini started the reading of a passage by Sylvio Pellico in the tenth grade where I went after leaving you; some of Mr. Bailly's students were entering, bumping into some of Mr. Bonnini's students who were coming out on the way back to their homeroom next door,

they returned to their seats, reopened their bags, took out books and notebooks for the history lesson.

When the class had settled down, after a few questions on the *Ancien Régime* and its difficulties, I told them about the beginnings of the French Revolution, the storming of the Bastille, the Declaration of the Rights of Man and of the Citizen, the King's escape and his arrest at Varennes.

Without leaving your seat you put your geography book and your notebook away in your bag, took out your *Excerpts of English Literature* which you opened at page 120, since you knew that you were going to start with *Julius Caesar*

(there was an engraving portraying the dictator and you wondered how this could possibly be the same man whose features you had tried to draw a little while ago, two floors above, under Mr. Martin's supervision; the two faces resembled each other so little),

while half of your classmates had gone out, some to go to the room next door which Mr. Bonnini had just entered, the others, who were taking German or Spanish, to return to their own classroom,

while other eleventh-graders, A1, B, C, or C1 or Modern came in to replace them, herded in by Mr. Bailly, who, tall and nervous in his light tweed suit, with his habitual air of exasperation, slammed the door behind him and threw his pigskin briefcase on the desk so violently that it caused immediate silence.

Your Uncle Henri was coming down the stairs. He nodded to the janitor, walked along the front of the Lycée, turned left toward the other door, the grade-school entrance, where Claude and François, his two youngest children, stood waiting for him as they did every day at the same time, unless your Aunt Rose came to pick them up and take them shopping somewhere.

He took them by the hand, passed in front of the beautiful glistening portal of Saint Hilaire, the tympanum of which, representing the resurrection of the dead, dates unfortunately from the 1890's, because the original—of which certain fragments can be seen at the Musée Cluny around the corner—was damaged during the Revolution,

emerged on the Boulevard Saint-Germain, where he had to wait several minutes before crossing, until the stream of cars had come to a stop at the red light, walked past the small garden in back of the illustrious abbatial church, the terraces of the Deux-Magots and of the Flore, past the small garden in back of the Ukrainian church, turned into the rue du Pré-aux-Clercs, climbed the six flights (no elevator in the old building); a visiting card bearing the name Henri Mouron was stuck on one of the doors on the fifth floor, but he did not notice it.

At first the two children chased each other up the steps, but they were soon out of breath; the smallest one had taken his father's hand again when they came into the kitchen where your Aunt Rose was ironing.

Two bowls of milk, bread and pieces of chocolate had been laid out on the table, on an oil cloth with small red and yellow squares.

The next day, yesterday, Tuesday, after lunch, after coffee, after a pipe, as he was standing already in his raincoat, holding François by the hand, your Aunt Rose, buttoning Claude's coat,

"Good Heavens; I think it's Pierre's birthday today."

"Pierre Vernier's?"

"No, no, no; your nephew's!"

"Hm; you must be right. He did give me a strange look this morning."

"You're his teacher, you see him almost every day, you can't forget that; he must have been very disappointed. . . ."

"But I couldn't say anything in front of his classmates. . . ."

"Why don't you ask him over for tea, I'll try to find something for him this afternoon when I take the children to the Bon Marché. Have you any idea what he might like?"

"The best would be to telephone him right now, but probably he's already left."

"Oh no, rue du Canivet is much closer to the Lycée than we are. He was born in 1939 I believe; that would make him fifteen."

You had not yet left; you had been allowed a cordial for the occasion, and you were savoring the last drops. Your father got up to answer, came back with a wide smile,

"For you, Pierre, your Uncle Henri."

You rushed to the phone.

"Hello, Pierre? It seems that you are fifteen years old today. Congratulations! You'll take your finals at sixteen, that's splendid. Listen, would you like to come over to our house this evening after school, for tea? Your aunt would be very pleased. We'll have a chat. You get out at five? After physics class. Fine. Well then, we'll expect you at five thirty. Is there something you might like? A book perhaps, or something else? Think about it. See you later."

You came back into the living room.

"Uncle Henri has invited me for tea this afternoon after school."

"That's very nice of him," said your mother; "remind him that we expect them for lunch on Thursday."

I got up; I buttoned my jacket.

"We'd better go, if you want to see your Uncle at school, before you go over to his house for tea. What are you studying right now? Rabelais? Goodbye Anne, goodbye Jean, all set then for tonight, he'll be my guest; I'll take him to a restaurant. Have him pick me up next door around seven."

We went downstairs, all four of us, around the apse of Saint Sulpice, up rue Saint-Hilaire where we saw your Uncle Henri coming toward us, having just left Claude and François at the grade-school entrance. We reached the janitor's lodge before him.

I let you go in and waited for him, watching you climb the stairs to your respective classrooms.

He said hello to me,

"It seems that our nephew Pierre is fifteen years old today; I had forgotten all about it. We're having him over for tea."

"He's spoiled."

He, too, went up the stairs; I crossed the courtyard to join my sixth-graders.

On their return from a trip, your parents decided that your brother Jacques should take Italian rather than English, like you and your older brother; he has handed Mr. Bonnini his homework:

"You are replying to an Italian friend who has asked you to give him a description of your family."

Your Uncle was listening to Denis Regnier read in a soft, very well articulated voice, with a certain pleasure to judge by his intonation:

". . . of all the herbs on earth, of all the metals hidden in unfathomable depths, of the precious stones of all the Orient and of the South, nothing shall be unknown to him."

In the amphitheatre, with all the curtains closed, your older brother was watching Mr. Hubert in the darkness demonstrate the existence of a focal point for spherical mirrors:

coming out of a projector encased in a metal box, two parallel beams lit up the chalk dust he was dropping from his hands, were reflected in a concave metal blade and came together.

I question Jean-Pierre Cormier, half hidden by Michel Daval, on the Renaissance. He answers:

"It is an educational reform."

"How so?"

"That's what Mr. Jouret told us."

"Mr. Jouret is certainly right, still, you'll have to explain to me a little what he meant by that, to see if you understood."

"It is the return to the study of Greek and Latin, to the humanities."

"Had they stopped studying Latin in the Middle Ages?"

"Oh no, all classes were held in Latin! But Greek was no longer being studied, and without Greek no man can a scholar be."

"I can see that Mr. Jouret is making you study your Rabelais. But, tell me, Mr. Cormier, why did they start studying Greek all of a sudden? Why does Gargantua insist on it so much in his letter to Pantagruel?"

"Because they wanted to rediscover antiquity."

"Had they forgotten all about it?"

"No, but the people of the Middle Ages did not consult the original texts, did not go to see the original statues; they were satisfied with what was said about them in the schools."

"And that was no longer enough?"

"No, because Constantinople had been taken by the Turks, because America had been discovered."

"How so?"

"Well, they were forced to recognize that the world was not as they had imagined it."

"And this change of the face of the earth necessitated an educational reform which took a very long time to materialize, which is perhaps only in its beginning stages today. Thank you."

Mr. Hutter, the German professor, is at the other end of the hall with his tenth-graders. I now know in what way he is related to his namesake Francis Hutter, in the first row before me, next to Alain Mouron, in front of Michel Daval. It goes rather far back: Frederic Hutter, grandfather of Mr. Alfred Hutter, had a first cousin, Emile Hutter, who was the great-grandfather of Francis. They had never seen each other before they met in class.

My next question is addressed to him. He raises his head, looking surprised.

"Well, aren't you going to stand up?"

He brushes back the reddish strand of hair hanging over his eyes.

"In what way did the Renaissance affect the fields of art and literature? Your book won't help you. I've already asked you to close it during question period, and your notebook too. That goes for everybody. Well? I'm waiting. What do you know about sixteenth-century painting?

"All countries began to imitate the Italians."

The door opens, an old man in a smock comes in, carrying a gigantic record book bound in black linen.

"Just a moment please."

I add my signature to your Uncle Henri's under the names of the absentees: Philippe Guillaume and André Knorr. There is a typewritten paper, which I take out and read to you:

"The Reverend Father Gollier, chaplain of the Lycée Taine, reminds you that religious instruction for all eleventh-graders takes place every Tuesday, from five to six."

I initial it. He goes away to the next class room, to your Uncle Henri.

"Well then, Hutter, what can you tell us about Italian painting? Surely you know a few names."

All eyes turn toward him, mockingly. He begins to twist his

fingers, bites his lips, frowns; all the others are amused. He bursts out, suddenly relaxing:

"Leonardo da Vinci."

"Fine, tell us about Leonardo da Vinci. . . . You know nothing about him? You don't know where he was born, where he died, how he lived, the names of some of his paintings, or if he did other things besides painting? No? Tell me about some other artist then."

He hangs his head, looks right and left as though calling for help. Why did he pick a seat in the first row if he counts on the others to prompt him? He must know something, but for the moment his mind is foggy; I can see that he's not going to utter another word, that he is resigning himself to what I'm going to tell him, that he'll make up for it some other time. I must try to remember to question him again on Saturday, or even tomorrow, in geography, on the year, the seasons, the day, the hour.

"I'm obliged to give you a zero. Sit down."

That was Tuesday and an hour later, in the amphitheatre on the third and highest floor

(through the window one could already see the sun going down, and brilliant yellow spots were appearing here and there on the tin roofs, and the clouds passed faster above the chimneys; Mr. Hubert's face and his smock looked as though they had been outlined on one side by a luminous ray; he was placing weights on a small platform, which was suspended from a cylindrical spring equipped with an indicator which moved along a graduated vertical ruler).

Alain Mouron, tired from his day, unable to understand why the professor insisted so much on notions that seemed extremely simple and plain to him, began doodling in his open book, blackening a detail on the first illustration of the chapter which was being explained, two circles representing the weights of a

dumbbell lifted, arms outstretched, by a large man in a bathing
suit, with the caption:

"The athlete makes a muscular effort,"
the last two words underlined.

Mr. Bailly has gone to pick up his two children at the grade-
school entrance.

They climbed down the steps of Saint-Hilaire station. He
had their family tickets punched; they stood waiting on the
Auteuil platform. A man was sleeping on a bench, under a big
poster that sang the praises of a powdered soup, a North
African, his face almost completely hidden under strips of
sticking plaster that made him a kind of mask with two blinders.
Many students were walking up and down, their arms full of
books, especially Africans and Orientals in groups. The train
in the opposite direction, to Austerlitz, pulled in and left again.
There was almost as large a crowd on the platform as before,
but they were no longer the same people and all, or almost all,
were rapidly walking toward the exit.

Michel Daval was not looking at the spring (dynamometer)
with which Mr. Hubert had just been playing, but at the Atwood
machine he had used during the previous lesson with his
elementary-math students to prove by experiment the fundamental principles of dynamics, and which he had pushed all
the way back to the end of the long table near the sink; on either
side of the pulley, the copper weights, suspended from nylon
threads, were oscillating slightly, noticeable only by the trembling, the scintillating of the small image of the windows
mirrored in them.

But a word in the lecture jerked him out of his fascination;
the professor had just said that the unit of force is one kilogram-
force or weight, namely the weight—in Paris—of an iridiated
platinum cylinder, deposited at the International Bureau of
Weights and Measures in Sèvres, because this reminded him
that a standard meter of iridiated platinum was also carefully

kept in Sèvres, and he wondered what this word "iridiated" which had not been explained might actually mean, hesitating to ask, since no one in the class had ever shown similar audacity, because Mr. Hubert had never encouraged them to ask questions; he finally consulted his book in which he found the following note:

"alloy of platinum and iridium, 10 per cent iridium."

Iridium, what could this substance be which he had never heard mentioned before, not even in the science-fiction stories, only now, because of an obscure adjective which had never stopped him up to this moment? Why had it been added to a metal as precious as platinum? Why did this kilogram have to consist of platinum? Was it only to show that this kilogram was unique, irreplaceable, that it had to be guarded as carefully as a royal crown or a talisman?

He imagined it sitting in a glass case in the center of a vast crypt behind huge doors with terrifying and complicated locks, around which carefully picked guards, armed with powerful revolvers, relieved each other continually, on a circular runway,

glowing in darkness and solitude, disturbed only by visits of a few scientists who had been promoted to the contemplation of the iridescent splendor, caused by the ten per cent of this mysterious iridium.

He had the impression of having just discovered one of the most fabulous secrets of science, accidentally, through the inadvertence of a book (who among his classmates suspected it? And the professor, Mr. Hubert, did he really know; he had slid over the word so casually, without seeming to give it the slightest importance?)

"all the metals hidden in unfathomable depths. . . ."

A little while ago, in the rue du Pré-aux-Clercs, your Uncle Henri closed his big Racine, Firmin Didot 1837 edition, in which he had just reread *Iphigénie:*

". . . to reward Achilles, to repay your good deeds."

He looked at the paper covering the boards; its pattern made one think of the sudden splattering of a windowpane covered by a thick layer of clay dust, with dirty rivulets and more resistant lumps; the once purple leather had turned olive green on the spine. He looked at his watch; about ten more minutes before he had to go. He stuffed his pipe and lit it, picked up one of the compositions you had handed in yesterday, on the subject:

"Describe the day of your vacation. . . ."

read a few lines, but it really bored him too much just at that moment; he put it back on the pile, went to leaf through the last issue of *Match* in the dining room near the radio, without stopping at any picture, not knowing what to do, finally, with these few moments of reprieve (your Aunt Rose had gone out);

he put his raincoat on, went down the six flights, and sat on the terrace of the Rouquet, at the corner of the boulevard and rue des Saints-Pères, to drink a coffee.

In the gymnasium you were straining your muscles as hard as you could, trying to climb a smooth rope, which you had trouble grasping with your feet (you should have worn different shoes); it was writhing like a snake, and the knot at the bottom was beating the sawdust in the basin; you still had over a yard to climb before you could touch the hook that had been screwed into the big green metal beam; Mr. Moret, in a blue shirt and shorts, bare-legged like a scout leader, little Mr. Moret who was the oldest of all your professors after Mr. Martin, was showing another group the movements he wanted to see them execute on the parallel bars.

In one of the classrooms on the ground floor I expounded to my seventh-graders on Justinian's great effort (it was our second history lesson) to reassemble the pieces of the shattered Roman Empire; I tried to give them some idea of poignant Byzantine splendor by describing my dream of Constantinople and Saint Sophia.

And now, Alain Mouron, who is sitting alone at the double desk in front of me because Francis Hutter is absent, as is André Knorr, carefully writes into his very clean notebook in an elegant, but already very cursive, hard-to-read handwriting, how one goes about determining one's position:

". . . in order to determine the meridian of one's position, one must know what time it is in Greenwich when it is noon in one's own location, which is usually quite easy; provided the weather is fair, the true noon, of course, the astronomical noon, the instant when the shadow is the shortest, not the conventional noon of the clocks. We already know that one hour's difference denotes a difference of fifteen degrees. . . ."

He stops writing; he wonders: but how does one find out what time it is in Greenwich? He hears me mention the radio. But what if the radio doesn't work any more, when one is at sea or in the middle of the desert, a large vessel or an airplane lost after a storm, and it is vital to determine which port or oasis is nearest, food and courage are giving out, well there is no means of knowing, all the maps one has are useless, useless all these efforts to find out, all this surveying; one is forced to go into the unknown like the first man; one risks starving to death a few miles from the richest depots. . . .

To measure the latitude; I draw a sextant on the blackboard; he no longer understands what I am saying, he has missed too much in between; he waits for me to finish with the parallels before going back to taking notes.

Mr. Bailly has just come home to rue Pierre-Leroux, after buying a pack of Gauloises (Wednesday is his day off); he is sitting at his table, before the mail which has piled up and which he ought to answer; he lights a cigarette. He, too, might have gone away somewhere, used these two days, Wednesday-Thursday, to avoid Elisabeth the way Elisabeth had avoided him Sunday-Monday, by fleeing to Orléans; take refuge at Claire's house? He would have had to ask the cook, who came in the morning only, to reserve her afternoon and pick up the children at their schools, since Elisabeth stays at the Lycée Aulnoy until five today.

". . . a globe"

(pointing to the one that is gathering dust on the wardrobe and that no one ever uses)

"is a faithful but impractical representation; one must have maps, but since it is impossible to make a section of a flat surface, no matter how small, coincide with a section of a spherical surface, there must necessarily be transposition, projection, according to different systems, all of which have their disadvantages, always deforming certain aspects, so that, for the study of a given field, one must always choose the most suitable and always be very suspicious, especially of maps that claim to represent the whole of the earth, and always try to keep in mind what sort of corrections one must make. . . ."

Michel Daval rummages in his bag, comes up with a pencil sharpener shaped like a tiny globe, rolls it over his notebook with his palm, goes on writing but can no longer keep on the lines, feels my eyes on him, closes his hand around the pencil sharpener (the words "Mercator projection" zigzag, the last letters growing larger), sits up, places the pencil sharpener in front of him, underlines what he has just written with a nice straight line, looks up at me, waits a second, wonders if he is going to get it, yes or no, bends over his notebook once more while pushing you with his elbow, as though you had bothered him.

by YVES BONNEFOY

Je te voyais courir sur des terrasses,
Je te voyais lutter contre le vent,
Le froid saignait sur tes lèvres.

Et je t'ai vue te rompre et jouir d'être morte ô plus belle
Que la foudre, quand elle tache les vitres blanches de ton sang.

II

L'été vieillissant te gerçait d'un plaisir monotone, nous
méprisions l'ivresse imparfaite de vivre.

"Plutôt le lierre," disais-tu, "l'attachement du lierre aux
pierres de sa nuit: présence sans issue, visage san racine.

"Dernière vitre heureuse que l'ongle solaire déchire, plutôt
dans la montagne ce village où mourir.

"Plutôt ce vent . . ."

III

Il s'agissait d'un vent plus fort que nos mémoires,
Stupeur des robes et cri des rocs—et tu passais devant ces
    flammes

La tête quadrillée les mains fendues et toute
En quête de la mort sur les tambours exultants de tes gestes.
C'etait jour de tes seins
Et tu régnais enfin absente de ma tête.

IV

Je me réveille, il pleut. Le vent te pénètre, Douve, lande résineuse endormie près de moi. Je suis sur une terrasse, dans un trou de la mort. De grands chiens de feuillages tremblent.

Le bras que tu soulèves, soudain, sur une porte, m'illumine à travers les âges. Village de braise, à chaque instant je te vois naître, Douve,

A chaque instant mourir.

by D'ELBERT E. KEENAN

I saw you running over the terraces,
I saw you wrestling with the wind,
The cold bled on your lips.

And I saw you break and take joy in being dead O more
beautiful
than the thunderbolt when it streaks the blank panes with your
blood.

II

The aging summer chapped you with dully repeated pleasures, we were scornful of the unfulfilled drunkenness of life.

"Rather the ivy," you said, "the clinging of the ivy to the
stones of the night: presence without issue, face without roots,

"Ultimate happy pane ripped by the claw of the sun, rather
in the mountains this village to die in,

"Rather this wind . . ."

III

We had in mind a wind stronger than our memories,
174

stupor of dresses and shout of rocks—and you passed in front
   of these flames,
your head checkered your hands cleft and all
of you questioning death on the exultant drumbeat of your
   gestures.

That was the day of your breasts
and you reigned at last absent from my head.

IV

    I awaken. The rain falls. The wind cuts through you, Douve,
pine-scented heath lying asleep beside me. I am on a terrace,
in a death hole. Great leafy dogs are atremble.

    The arm you lift, suddenly, toward a door, lights me through
the ages. Village of glowing coals, at every instant I see you
born, Douve,

    At every instant die.

New French Poetry

by GERMAINE BRÉE

And I am re-begot
Of absence, death; things which are not.
                              JOHN DONNE

We, the children of Hiroshima . . .
                              PIERRE EMMANUEL

Ronsard, Verlaine, Neveux, Laforgue, Mallarmé; Apollinaire, Reverdy, Claudel, Péguy, Valéry; Jouve, Supervielle, Eluard, Ponge, Michaux, St.-John Perse; Césaire, Char, Emmanuel. . . . In this *"versant de l'âge"* (Emmanuel), the young poets of France have no easy heritage, advancing as they are on a tide of poetry unprecedented perhaps in the long history of French letters.

Not the least among the problems faced by the present generation of poets is that of finding its own voice and idiom, its forms and themes, while still in the presence of as forceful a creator as St.-John Perse, as exacting a craftsman as Char, as vigorous a predecessor as Emmanuel. Unlike the surrealists, the younger poets do not decry their predecessors. In *Poèmes de l'Année*, an annual anthology published since 1955, which groups the best poems of the year, Jouve, St.-John Perse, Cocteau, Ponge, Michaux etc., appear side by side with some fifty other poets, respected, read and even admired.

Nor have there been any startling manifestoes. Only in the last two or three years have a few of the younger poets started to formulate for themselves and their readers what they expect of poetry and the poet: here again they are fully aware of the century of discussion and theory which lies behind them, going back to Baudelaire. In articles dispersed in magazines like *Les Lettres Nouvelles, L'Age Nouveau, Les Cahiers du Sud,* in *Yale French Studies* and other scholarly reviews; in prefaces to books, or as part of a volume of verse; often in the poems themselves, Yves Bonnefoy, Alain Bosquet, Jean-Claude Ibert, André Marissel, Claude Vigée have spoken of the nature and function of poetry and the poet. But each only for himself. The present group of poets is not given to dogmatic statement, preferring rather slow and cautious formulation, just as it shuns the "school" or group. Only now, through individual ties of friendship, does it seem to be recovering from the centrifugal force of the war.

Leaving aside the much discussed child prodigy, Minou Drouet—hardly a characteristic case—the "young" poets of France, sometimes designated as the "generation of 1925", can be more or less accurately defined as those who are now in their middle or late thirties: Yves Bonnefoy, Alain Bosquet, André du Bouchet, Edouard Glissant, Edmond Jabès, Philippe Jaccottet, Jean Laude, André Marissel, Rouben Mélik, Henri Pichette, Charles le Quintrec, Armen Tarpinian, Claude Vigée, Kateb Yacine. . . . Not too far removed are some slightly older poets—Jean Grosjean (b. 1912) and Pierre Emmanuel (b. 1916)—and some newcomers—Pierre Oster (b. 1933) and Marc Alyn (b. 1937).

No group of poets, perhaps, has found it as easy generally to reach publishers. Poetry, new poetry, is fairly welcome today in Paris, perhaps because, after the war, Pierre Seghers, a poet himself, showed how well poetry could sell: his successful *"Poètes d'aujourd'hui"* series no doubt finances the ever growing collection of bi-monthly *"cahiers"* in which hundreds of indistinguishable young poets appear. Recently the *Mercure de France* has shown a renewed interest in poetry, picking up its old tradition of symbolist days, while Gallimard and the Editions du Seuil have launched their own collections of contemporary poetry. Anthologies of "new poetry" (1952; 1955), the annual *Poèmes de l'Année* series, reviews of books of verse in magazines with a fairly wide distribution give most poets some chance of reaching at least one reader. It is curious to note that, unlike the surrealists, the young poets seem anxious to reach a wider public, to be understood. Bosquet, Marissel, Vigée are perspicacious critics and Bosquet a fairly impartial editor also.

Amid the wide diversity of names and publications, how possible is it to trace paths or distinguish trends? Quite clearly certain influences are at work: Char's in the aphorisms and elliptic images of du Bouchet and Tarpinian, Claudel's and St.-John Perse's in Edouard Glissant's epic vision and stanza, in Jean Laude's poem of the sea, *Les Saisons et la mer,* as in some of Oster's great odes. A surrealist still lives in Alain Bosquet, Eluard in Rouben Mélik's verse, while Emmanuel and Jouve are present everywhere. But du Bouchet's imagery is his, not Char's; and the great rhythmical sweep of St.-John Perse is present nowhere nor Emmanuel's powerful rhetoric and prophetic vision.

The most widespread instrument of today's poet is free verse, sensitive liquid verse which is frequently designated in such titles as *"Chant"* or *"Chanson"*—song. Deliberately, it would seem, these poets have turned away from preoccupations with form, striving rather to *"retrouver la parole"* (Roger Giroux)— "recover speech." They tend to prefer more limpid images, more simple vocabulary, a direct, less intellectual expression of emotion.

In many instances they move toward the traditional stanza forms: Oster will, for example, try the formal Pindaric ode; Jaccottet prefers the sonnet form; Bosquet, in *Le Premier Testa-*

ment, uses the regularly rimed four-line stanza. Vigée is moving away from free verse toward regular alexandrines, grouped in ample stanzas. Charles le Quintrec and Jean-Claude Renard rely almost completely on the forms inherited from the pre-symbolist era. But, as is the case with Jaccottet, these forms are very freely handled, or, as is the case with Bosquet, they serve to bring out the singularly untraditional mood of the poem. On the whole, however, these poets are lyrical rather than intellectual, somewhat diffident with regard to form, standing poised between two dangers: the formlessness and abundance of an all-too-facile lyricism; an easy virtuosity in the handling of traditional forms. For the reader, they often have the charm, at first reading, of the familiar, a charm enhanced, for the better poets, by the fact that this first impression is deceptive.

Before trying further to distinguish the best among these poets, one might say that there is an atmosphere common to most: a muted note; sadness rather than revolt or despair; a familiarity with the thought and carnal reality of death, which seems to carry with it no deep sense of tragedy, no ultimate revulsion or terror as it did with a Villon; a curiously melancholy, sensual, sexual form of love in which the blending of two bodies, their sensuous closeness offers a momentary haven against distress. There is nothing sordid in this love, almost similar in kind to the sensuous tenderness the poet feels toward flowers, rain, water, the natural world.

Underlying this theme, explaining it no doubt, one finds over and over again a recurrent, obsessive imagery: blood, wounds, rust and decay; crumbling walls and statues; dead museums; night; dark, still waters which mirror nothing; ashes and the slow immersion of things in sand or slime; the blighted lightning-struck tree, or the tree still standing but rootless, Marissel's "tree without roots." Human beings here lose their faces, are transformed into slime, caught in tangled grass or roots. Mute and faceless wanderers, they move along roads that lead nowhere or take trains that reach dead stations overrun by grass; or they float in frail skiffs made of bark, oars abandoned, among tangled grass. "Night has closed in upon one, where one travels," writes du Bouchet, almost summarizing this imagery, and Marissel: "Our life is rooted in the depths of stagnant ponds."

This is quite clearly an imagery of fear—not a personal, individual fear but the sense of a universal threat present in the subconscious depths of the poet's sensitivity, a threat to all human beings but also to all things on our planet, a blight moving, spreading over the planet. The "I" of the poet becomes "one," becomes one too with the flower, the fruit, the wave. "Today," writes Laude, "all beauty arrays itself in the prestige of that which will blight it." Certainly no generation before has felt quite in the same way the imminence of a "mute world," or a total destruction of our planet with its seasons, and rhythms and metamorphoses. "We cannot even imagine that beauty will triumph," continues Laude, "and that triumphant, we could enjoy it without distress." The great epic of man and the creation, St.-John Perse's fundamental theme, is alien to these poets. Other poets have celebrated or denounced this earth, described it, finding it beautiful or hostile, or they have sought to destroy it, like Mallarmé, replacing it by another acceptable to "*l'esprit*," but none as yet have looked at it with a tenderness born of the vulnerability it shares with us, and the sense of our fraternal responsibility for its existence. The poet, today, must *preserve:* preserve the tree, the flower, the animal. "The need to redefine the essential relationship of man with the world that surrounds him," writes Alain Bosquet, ". . . is an important phenomenon of our time. It is not the only one; it is accompanied by another, the need to give back to the cosmos a place which . . . was snatched away from it at the time when man appeared to be the unchallenged monarch of his planet. Since Hiroshima . . . our disappearance as an animal species is incontrovertible. Our collective suicide, through a simple miscalculation or an act of banditism, is not impossible. As a result . . . we feel bonds of solidarity, not so much with our fellow men as with our shrunken habitat and with what it was before we put in an appearance. Something impels us to love plants (after all they may, perhaps, survive us); stones (after all they may survive plants); the sun (but of course it will survive both plant and stone)." "We are getting closer to the earth," writes du Bouchet, "not to the sky." Small wonder too, as Bosquet points out, that our earth, in the poets' imagery, has become a room, one room with its familiar objects or with its one burning light beyond which we can take only a step or two, gazing over large flat expanses, sparsely ploughed fields, deserts over which reigns an icy cold light, or darkness.

This, in essence, is the universe which appears in du Bouchet's sparse verse (*L'air; Sans Couvercle; Le Moteur blanc*). The earth, his habitat, is an almost empty whitewashed room, beyond which stretches a universe of stone, fire and glass, a devastated universe: "All that remains after fire, the disqualified stones, the cold stones, the small change of ashes in the field." The soles of one's shoes remain glued to the road and "the cloud covers the road with a black cloud." Words here are "lost stones": "This text like a lost stone, wrenched a second time from the earth in the room that enrobes me." The poet's task here is well-nigh impossible. "Each brilliant word is consumed in a perfume of derision" leaving him in solitude. ". . . I live within myself in a mute world." In this world "there exists only one sentence which has not yet been deciphered" and a man who "sees almost nothing." We are at the very confines of T. S. Eliot's spiritual *Wasteland*. Du Bouchet's technique and universe are well suited to each other, but neither escapes the dangers of obscurity and monotony. Du Bouchet is close to the hermetic and incommunicable or even to the refusal of all language.

To the "derision" that our condition places upon the poet's most "brilliant" word, Alain Bosquet gives another answer. Poetry, he claims, after the surrealists, is not the poem, much less is it literature. Poetry is an attitude, a contestation, the perpetual calling into question of all affirmation. "It is useless," Bosquet makes poetry say, "to build for yourself a mental shelter of your aversions and seductions, of your will and your cowardice; as soon as I appear, your fragile castle collapses." And so the poem is built in a perpetual contestation between the word and the thing to which it refers, between the poet and the word, the poem and the poet. This double movement of affirmation and destruction sweeps right through Bosquet's *Le Premier Testament,* held within the familiar, traditional verse-form it contradicts, naming all objects, all feelings, all themes in a continual and free "allegro" and contrapuntal development— poem is born from the impossibility of writing a poem.

I say yes to love; which I can't understand.
. . . .
I say yes to the poem; it leaves only ashes
. . . .
I say no to the apple-tree; I want only its bark.
. . . .
I say "apple" to the apple; it answers "you lie." . . . etc.

There is, for the reader, both esthetic and intellectual pleasure, emotion and amusement in this game involving the world, the poet and the poem, a game from which the poem emerges triumphant, leaving the "poet" as its "first will" and testament, leaving us empty-handed but with a feeling of freedom and ironic joy.

In this lightness of touch and freedom of movement, Bosquet

stands almost alone, closer in spirit to the poet and novelist Queneau than to his contemporaries.

"I should like," writes Bonnefoy, "to unite, I should like almost to identify poetry and hope. But that it should be by some hard path, since there are two sorts of poetry, one being chimerical, deceptive and fatal—just as there are two sorts of hope." Hope in our time must find its foundation. "It is easy to be a poet among the gods. But we have come after the gods. We cannot have recourse to heaven in order to guarantee the poetic transmutation and we are forced to question its seriousness. . . . What really do we value? . . . I am certain that modern poetry—poetry without the gods . . . must know what it wants so that it can, in full awareness, measure the power of words." Of all the young poets Bonnefoy is the closest to the tradition of Baudelaire and Mallarmé, the most deeply thoughtful, the most conscious that we are confronting as crucial a *"table rase"* of all the notions our minds formerly harbored as has ever been experienced before. We must, says Bonnefoy, "reinvent the few elementary gestures which link us to things in the incessant cold dawn of a life preoccupied by the absolute." For Bonnefoy, humanity today is still in search of a lost absolute. "Why do we like lighted lamps in empty rooms, statues whose faces have been worn away by sand, dead cloisters? Is it some form of beauty—so-called—that we are looking for on these shores? No, but eternity which we have in common." But for the moment, what Bonnefoy sees as the poet's task is that he assert "wildly" what is here and now, the most living "things on this earth": "the tree," "the human face," "the stone," "the wind," "the earth," "water," "fire." The poet's universe today can only be the universe of him who waits, the "wanderer" waiting for the passage of the Grail. The poet is he who is present and, being present, asserts that the Grail itself is there.

The images and themes suggested above are those which order Bonnefoy's two long poems: *Du Mouvement et de l'im-*

mobilité de Douve (see page 172) and *Hier régnant désert.*
Both retrace an adventure, a descent into death and a meta-
morphosis. What is "Douve"? Moat or woman or poetry? Torn
to shreds, disintegrated, a presence luminous nonetheless, and
eternal, "our force and glory." The evocation power of Bonnefoy's sometimes obscure imagery, the quality of the tonalities
used, muted and yet intense, the architectural strength of his
poems place him in the foremost rank among the younger poets.

A quest too is the theme which directs the movement of Jean
Laude's *Les Saisons et la mer,* but a quest in a more brilliant
world, lighted by the movement of a sun, "rising, moving to its
zenith and declining," as the poet sets off on a journey to the
very source of time, confronted all the way by the presence of
death, death at last incarnated in the myth of Iseut. Iseut who,
like Douve, lives forever through her own recurring death.

Against the background of history and of our earth, Glissant
in *Les Indes*—a poem in six cantos—evokes the story of
Columbus, as Claudel had done before him. Born in Martinique,
he recreates the great epic adventure of two worlds from the
point of view of "the Indies" of the red man, colonized and
destroyed, and of the black brought into servitude. An ethnol-
ogist and historian, Glissant brings to his poem his knowledge
of the facts of the conquest, but seen through their consequences:
a world united but in fear. Yet behind it lies a dream, symbolized
in the islands, the "Indies," perpetually destroyed and incessantly reborn, the dream which now the red man and the black
man are carrying back to the white man, their tormentor: the
dream of a universal love. Less imperious than St.-John Perse,
more immediately human in his tone, Glissant blends together
the themes of strife, suffering and death, of destruction, meta-
morphosis and rebirth. Beyond his vision of the great collective
movement of our time—the emancipation of the non-European
peoples—his poem evokes the epic spiritual adventure of all
humanity:

"But perhaps, whoever he may be, man always has only the same desire, the same ardor? And, whatever his origin, the same known suffering? What Indies draw him on? Or, even though his dream be but passionate reason, what ocean obtrudes between it and him? No man can answer with certainty; yet each attempts another crossing. The sea is eternal."

No other poet has succeeded, as has Glissant, in so triumphantly combining his concern with an immediate social and humanitarian issue and the exigencies of poetic expression.

Concerned too with man's suffering and hope, cruelty and capacity for love are the young Christian poets who, following in the wake of Emmanuel and Grosjean, think and feel in "planetary" universal terms.

The young Protestant poet, André Marissel, in *L'Homme et l'abîme* ("Man and the Abyss") records a personal spiritual descent into hell, one which, however, involves all men and develops in the menacing darkness cast by the imminence of a nuclear catastrophe. In the abyss of darkness where he is plunged, the poet experiences the existence of a presence felt as a living certainty. The tree, rooted in darkness, becomes, in Marissel's verse, the visible guarantee of the permanent life of a humanity, itself rooted in the darkness of an existence which is symbolized by the cross, the eternal tree of crucifixion. The poet's descent into the abyss is an "imitation" of Christ's. He is the bearer of a hard-won and difficult certainty which he brings to all men.

In direct contrast to Marissel's tense, tight verse, often abstract almost to the point of prosaism, is Charles le Quintrec's luminous, natural universe teeming with life: bees, birds, flowers, fields, woods, sea, sun, men and women. God is present everywhere in this universe. In each poem, the poet rediscovers a garden of Eden. Even if "the hour of the curfew circles our planet," the poet accepts it not as an end but as a beginning for a new man whose "flesh will be spiritual." Charles le Quintrec's poems reveal a violent, personal love of the earth, a sense of the beauty of each separate creature, from blade of grass to woman. What is most interesting perhaps in his verse, besides the dynamic certainty of the tone which comes, no doubt, from his faith, is its fresh sensuality and rich, direct imagery. His very qualities, however, sometimes lead him to rely on rather facile rhetorical forms of neoromantic verse, a temptation to which another talented young Catholic poet, Jean-Claude Renard, frequently yields—the price paid, perhaps, for certainty.

Less ambitious in their themes, speaking only for themselves even when preoccupied with the destiny of all men, each "building" his own *"demeure"* (home) upon the earth, are the lyrical poets Edmond Jabès (*Je bâtis ma demeure*), Philippe Jaccottet (*L'Effraie* and *L'Ignorant*), Rouben Mélik (*Le Chant réuni*), Armen Tarpinian (*Le Chant et l'ombre*) and Claude Vigée (*L'Eté indien*). Each one of them in his way has turned to poetry in order to go beyond the brutal surface of a senseless reality; each one attempts, through the poem, to combat the forces of death and darkness they experience within and around them. All are aware that French poetry must move away from a long attrition caused in part by the ruthless surrealist attack on language, in part by the doubt cast upon the validity of all human activities—poetry among them—in the light of the history of the last half century. These poets are not content to be "poets of famine," as Claude Vigée would say, poets of refusal and despair. Each in his own manner approaches the "heart rending inner consent to human history" of which Vigée speaks. In *L'Eté indien* Vigée has most honestly, most clearly defined the hesitations he faces, his doubts and sense of responsibility as he stands between "the shadow" and "the song" (Tarpinian). Of these poets, Jaccottet is closer to the "shadow." His subtly complex rhythms and highly modern use of traditional forms such as the sonnet; his preoccupation with death, decay and love; the interweaving of a rich imagery with the haunting sense of impending doom—all recall the baroque or metaphysical poets of the late Renaissance. Rouben Mélik, in contrast, is the poet of simple assertions, of "the time of life," of the "opera of our joy." He does not forget that "blood has flowed," nor the "weight of shadow and mystery," nor the "lost cry" of the man about to be hanged. But, in very limpid, fluid verse he speaks of "the stone," "the tree," of the "future vigil and the future hope!" From New England, where he now lives, Claude Vigée brings a wealth of imagery culled from the peaceful American countryside. An exile from his native Alsace, he records in his verse those moments of joy often reached in love, the love of wife or children, the love of the earth, moments when man and the cosmos achieve a fragile harmony and the earth is "truly at home in the heart of man." The victory is hard-won and temporary, but for an instant "exile" gives way to a sense of plenitude.

French poetry seems cautiously oriented in this direction. It is always dangerous and, perhaps, useless to try to determine "trends" in poetry, particularly contemporary. But the youngest among these poets, Marc Alyn, still in his early twenties, most vigorously asserts the power of joy, the power of light against an ever present inhuman darkness and death. Poetry for him is obviously an act of faith in being, in feeling, in speaking. Like Mélik or Vigée, Alyn is willing—sometimes a little too willing —to trust the spontaneous expressions, images and rhythms that come to him easily and abundantly.

Though it often still moves in the shadow of death, one senses no bitter revolt in this poetry, no deeply tragic tone even. It expresses fundamentally an acceptance, not a facile one, but still an acceptance of life, language and humanity. It is moving away from the restricted realm of a du Bouchet—restricted in both theme and language. "I see almost nothing . . . ," writes du Bouchet, "I should like to step out of life for an instant"; while in sharp contrast, Marc Alyn writes, "I speak the world, with the world as my inkwell." And "To hope is to have humanity in one's veins."

FROM La Révocation
de L'edit de Nantes, a novel

by PIERRE KLOSSOWSKI

translated by ANNE BORCHARDT

(*Roberte's diary, May 1954*)

. . . I jumped onto the platform of a bus, the first one to come
by, and leaned out, musing as I watched the stores pass, when
an unexpected contact forced me to go sit down inside. . . .
As he did not stop staring at me, I got up and left the bus at the
Théâtre Français. Passing through the portico of the Palais-
Royal, I entered the Montpensier arcade. Inside the arcade,
practically deserted at that hour, footsteps were echoing mine,
coming closer: I was being followed, nothing unusual for a
Member of Parliament. The man—a kind of fat, hairless giant,
the typical petty spy—would stop two or three shopwindows
away each time I glanced into one or another of the stores.
Where was the new shirtmaker that Gilberte had told me about?
Finally I passed under the arch of the Beaujolais arcade: that's
where it was, on the right. But by now the giant had overtaken
me. I pushed open a glass door, I had made a mistake—this
store was only being remodeled—the man came in behind me.
Although the people outside, strolling about or standing in front
of the stalls of the bookstore opposite, could have seen through
188

the half-frosted windows anything abnormal happening in the empty store, no one thought of it for a moment. His back against the glass door, the giant blocked my way as soon as I tried to leave, my hand on the door knob. Then, through a door at the back of the store, appeared another man, of medium height, stocky, in shirt sleeves. They stared at each other with a look of agreement. The second man withdrew and left the inside door half open. . . .

. . . Less than an hour later, my temples throbbing, I sat down on the terrace of the Régence. My hands must have been trembling and the waiter immediately asked me if there was anything wrong. I smiled, got up to go to the washroom, looked in the mirror: no reason to make up again, I looked extremely well. After all, what exactly could I blame them for? If they had tasted a pitiful pleasure. . . . For me the pleasure had just begun. I returned to my table and went over everything again. While I was on the platform of the bus—my back against the railing, my arm raised, my hand wandering along the pole— the giant, who had first chatted with the conductor, took hold of my fingers. I went inside and looked for an empty seat: but then he came and sat down opposite me, staring at me in the most insolent way. I was sitting with my hands lying flat on the leather seat, perhaps my legs were spread apart, and a smile hovered on my lips as I felt the warm breeze through the open window. Did I keep smiling, my lips parted, while he stared more insistently? At least I immediately crossed my legs, I folded my hands. After all, I did have my Legion of Honor rosette in the lapel of my suit. At that moment, I decided to get off the bus and, I remember, I pulled off the rosette and stuck it in my purse. I nonchalantly crossed the square in front of the Théâtre Français, I entered the Palais-Royal and so on up to the arch of the Beaujolais arcade. . . . And now I tried to figure out the stages of the creature's itinerary. He was attracted to me. He had to touch my fingers, and from then on there was no way for him to stop before his descent into the basement. From the moment of that furtive but irrepressible contact, what scene, at once rapid and detailed, must have unfolded in his brain? Or had there only been, all along, the image of those parallel bars and the fear that they would remain until evening in useless rigidity? Afterwards, when he was on his knees in front of me, when I was exposed and reduced to helplessness, had the two images: that of the beautiful stranger with the Legion of Honor and that of the same woman, now bound and hanging by her hands—had these images merged into one, or did they conflict enough to produce the emotion that was swelling his sad face? Once he got off the bus, after following closely enough to watch me stroll ahead of him through the Palais-Royal arcades, having already "contacted" the skin of my fingers, he was probably elaborating on that first sensation, extending it to my whole body which he imagined, studying the movement of my hips, my possible positions in the imminent situation he knew would be unexpected and inconceivable for me and therefore all the more urgent for him . . . until the moment when he couldn't do anything but corner me in that empty store. Almost dazed, how he stared at my hand on the knob of the door that he prevented me from reopening, while the stocky man loomed up through the other door, that fatal door left ajar on the gloomy staircase! Noticing an exit on the upper landing, which probably led to the rue de Beaujolais, I tried to make a dash for it. But the stocky man, who was waiting for me on the stairs, brought his hand down on my fingers clutching the banister; but still thinking I could escape, I jerked my hand away, walked down again and—two steps from the back room of the shop, that moment when, still resolved to defend myself, striking the giant in the face with my handbag, I saw him crouch, almost collapsing . . . when, already under my skirt, his hand stole between the garter and the skin, grasped the fleshiest part of my thigh, his arm encircled my legs, lifted me, swung me over his shoulder, a movement so sudden and unexpected that I had to catch hold of his neck with both hands—and then his crazy descent with me, down the spiral staircase to the basement. The other man, who had preceded him, was already pushing open the heavy steel door into a neon-lighted room with glaring walls. The linoleum on the floor gleamed, and beneath enormous fans whirring on the ceiling, among all kinds of gymnasium apparatus, the sight of the parallel bars, equipped with thongs. . . . To think that just a short time before I had been idly sauntering between the Opéra and the Théâtre Français, while those bars were waiting for me! Here I was, attached by the wrists, my moist hands smelling of lotion in the suffocating air despite the fans, my perfect and useless fingernails. . . . Without paying any attention to the upper part of my body or taking off my gray suit jacket, they unzipped my skirt and pulled off everything else. I was still kicking; they tied my ankles, one at each end of the vertical bars—and all this in complete silence, a silence consisting of my own dumbness in virtual complicity with the two men, as if our panting replaced the words we might have exchanged. The giant brought his mouth to one of my bound hands and, as I clenched my fist, he unfolded and straightened my fingers, moved them between his lips and sucked my fingernails with great application. Then, having caught his breath, staggering and sweating, leaning on the bar, he stuck out his tongue which twisted in a pathetic effort and only managed to brush slowly against my wide-open palm. Finally his tongue settled there and began titillating faster and faster. I still turned my head away. . . . Soon I could no longer control myself, uselessly trying to raise my knee so my thigh would hide the irresistible effects. "Turn off the lights at least," I said in a voice no longer mine, while the stocky man facing me ostentatiously exhibited a card and slid it into my handbag. But the lights stayed on and, my eyes closed, under the whirring of the ceiling fans, I abandoned myself in front of those two strangers. . . . The relief I then felt in opening up, in letting myself go at last under their eyes in that impossible position. . . . A heavy, dull noise at my feet. I reopened my eyes. The giant had fallen. The stocky man lifted him under the arms and led him away, staggering. For more than a minute I remained there, bound, alone, unquestionably the least pleasant moment of what I cannot even call a nightmare. And I was almost reassured to see the second man appear again, slowly, his hands in his pockets—a blond boy with a crew cut, prominent eyes, an intelligent expression. His shirt was impeccably white and his hands, which he just then took out of his pockets to untie me, were very neat, a bracelet on his left wrist. He turned away while I fixed my skirt, went to get my handbag, gave it back to me, and offered me a glass of cognac. But I slapped him. Then he snatched away my skirt again, stepped on it, put his hands back in his pockets, and, without flinching, received another slap; and with that I couldn't stop until I lost consciousness. . . . Actually, what could a woman do in such a situation? . . . Scream, of course, rouse the whole building—in so lively a neighborhood—but we women who once organized "charity," we women who are now at the controls of the nation, we women who "have seen too much"— if we happened to be beautiful, if we happen to be beautiful still—we have no choice but to be silent. Make an investigation? Because of this card that reproduces . . . my fingerprints? To get to the root of it? Just to give some work to that good-for-nothing C——— at police headquarters? Nonsense! But to go back, one of these days, to the scene, to caress with my own hands those parallel bars to which they were so well fastened . . . that is another story. This special opportunity to be myself, from the moment I got on the first bus that came by to the moment in that basement when I found myself hanging and shaken, this opportunity then is nothing more nor less than the taut bow of my meditation upon an idle afternoon. How delicious that pastry tasted! How soothing the fall of the fountains under the sycamore trees! How exquisite this city in its flow! . . .

Sonnet

by PHILIPPE JACCOTTET

Comme je suis un étranger dans notre vie,
je ne parle qu'à toi avec d'étranges mots,
parce que tu seras peut-être ma patrie,
mon printemps, nid de paille et de pluie aux rameaux,

ma ruche d'eau qui tremble à la pointe du jour,
ma naissante Douceur-dans-la-nuit . . . (Mais c'est l'heure
que les corps heureux s'enfouissent dans leur amour
avec des cris de joie, et une fille pleure

dans la cour froide. Et toi? Tu n'es pas dans la ville,
tu ne marches pas à la rencontre des nuits,
c'est l'heure où seul avec ces paroles faciles

je me souviens d'une bouche réelle . . .) O fruits
mûrs, source des chemins dorés, jardins de lierre,
je ne parle qu'à toi, mon absente, ma terre . . .

English Translation

by D'ELBERT E. KEENAN

Because a stranger in our life I stand,
To you alone with these strange words I sing,
Since you perhaps will be my fatherland,
My nest of straw, rain in the branches, spring,
My trembling water-hive at break of day,
My Sweetness-in-the-night a-borning. (Now
With joyous cries, blithe bodies bore their way
Deep, deep into their love, all heedless how
A girl weeps in the cold. And you? Nightfall
Awaits your steps no more, nor city street.
Alone with facile words now, I recall
A living mouth.) I speak to you, ripe sweet
Fruits, fount of golden roads, leafed garden wall,
You only, absent one, my earth, my all.

FROM In the Labyrinth, a novel

_____

by ALAIN ROBBE-GRILLET

_____

translated by RICHARD HOWARD

The picture, in its varnished wood frame, represents a tavern
scene. It is a nineteenth-century etching, or a good reproduction
of one. A large number of people fills the taproom: a crowd of
drinkers sitting or standing and, on the far left, the innkeeper
standing on a slightly raised platform behind his counter.

The innkeeper is a fat, bald man wearing an apron. He leans
forward, both hands resting on the counter's edge, over several
half-full glasses that have been set there, his massive shoulders
turned toward a small group of burghers in frock coats who
appear to be engaged in an animated discussion; standing in
various attitudes, many are making expansive gestures that
sometimes involve their whole bodies and are doubtless extremely expressive.

To their right—that is, in the center of the print—several
groups of drinkers are sitting at tables irregularly arranged—
or rather, crammed—in a space too small to hold them all
comfortably. These men too are making extravagant gestures
and their faces are violently contorted, but their movements,
like their expressions, are suspended and set, which makes their
meaning uncertain too; particularly since the words being
shouted on all sides seem to have been absorbed by a thick

layer of glass. Some men, in the intensity of their feelings, have half risen from their chairs or their benches and are pointing above the intervening heads toward a more remote interlocutor. Everywhere hands are raised, mouths open, heads turn; fists are clenched, pounded on tables or brandished in mid-air.

At the far right a group of men, almost all in work clothes like those sitting at the tables, have their backs to the latter and are crowding around some poster or picture tacked on the wall. A little in front of them, between their backs and the first row of drinkers facing in the other direction, a boy is sitting on the floor among all these legs with their shapeless trousers, all these clumsy boots stamping about and trying to move toward his left; on the other side he is partially protected by the bench. The child is drawn facing straight ahead. He is sitting with his legs folded under him, his arms clasped around a large box something like a shoebox. No one is paying any attention to him. Perhaps he was knocked down in the confusion. As a matter of fact, in the foreground, not far from where he is sitting, a chair has been overturned and is still lying on the floor.

Somewhat apart, as though separated from the crowd surrounding them by an unoccupied zone—narrow, of course, but nevertheless wide enough for their isolation to be noticeable, in any case wide enough to call attention to them though they are in the background—three soldiers are sitting around a smaller table, the second from the rear on the right, their motionlessness and their rigidity in violent contrast with the civilians who fill the room. The soldiers are looking straight ahead, their hands resting on the checkered tablecloth; there are no glasses in front of them. They are the only men whose heads are not bare, for they are wearing low-peaked police caps. Behind them, at the extreme rear, the last seated drinkers are mingled with others standing, forming a jumbled mass; besides, the drawing here is vaguer too. Under the print, in the white margin, someone has written a title: "The Defeat of Reichenfels."

On closer examination, the isolation of the three soldiers seems to result less from the narrow space between them and the crowd than from the direction of the glances around them. All the figures in the background look as if they were passing— or trying to pass, for the space is cramped—behind them to reach the left side of the picture, where there is probably a door (though this hypothetical exit cannot be seen in the picture because of a row of coat racks loaded with hats and coats); every head is looking straight ahead (that is, toward the coat racks), an occasional exception turning to speak to someone who has remained in the rear. Everyone in the crowd gathered on the right is looking toward the right wall. The drinkers at the tables are represented in natural poses, turning toward the center of each group or else toward one neighbor or another. As for the burghers in front of the counter, they too are completely absorbed in their own conversation, and the innkeeper leans toward them without paying any attention to the rest of his customers. Among the various groups circulate a number of persons not yet settled, but obviously soon about to adopt one of several probable attitudes: either examining the poster, sitting down at one of the tables, or else going out behind the coat racks; a moment's scrutiny is enough to reveal that each has already determined what he is going to do next; here as among the groups, no face, no movement betrays hesitation, perplexity, inner vacillation or contradiction. The three soldiers, on the contrary, seem forsaken. They are not talking to each other; they are not looking at anything in particular: neither glasses, nor poster, nor their neighbors. They have nothing to do. No one looks at them and they themselves have nothing to look at. The position of their faces—one full front, the other in profile, the last in a three-quarters view—indicates no common subject of attention. Besides, the first man—the only one whose features are completely visible—betrays no expression whatever, merely a fixed, vacant stare.

The contrast between the three soldiers and the crowd is further accentuated by a precision of line, a clarity in rendering, much more evident in their case than in that of other individuals the same distance from the viewer. The artist has shown them with as much concern for detail and almost as much sharpness of outline as if they were sitting in the foreground. But the composition is so involved that this is not apparent at first glance. Particularly the face shown full front has been portrayed with a wealth of detail that seems quite out of proportion to the indifference it expresses. No specific thought can be attributed to it: it is merely a tired face, rather thin and narrowed further by several days' growth of beard. This thinness, these shadows that accentuate the features without, on the other hand, indicating the slightest individual characteristic nevertheless emphasize the brilliance of the wide-open eyes.

The military overcoat is buttoned up to the neck, where the regimental number is embroidered on a folded tab of the same material. The cap is set straight on the head, covering the hair, which is cut extremely short, judging from its appearance at the temples. The man is sitting up straight, his hands lying flat on the table that is covered with a red-and-white-checkered cloth.

He has finished his drink some time ago. He doesn't look as if the notion of leaving had occurred to him. Yet around him the café's last customers have vanished. The light is dim now: the proprietor turned out most of the lamps before leaving the room himself.

The soldier, eyes wide, continues to stare into the half-darkness a few yards in front of him, where the child is standing, motionless too, his arms stiff alongside his body. But it is as if the soldier didn't see the child—or anything else. He looks as if he had fallen asleep from exhaustion, sitting close to the table, his eyes wide open.

It is the child who speaks first. He says, "Are you asleep?" He has spoken almost in a whisper, as if he were afraid to waken the sleeper. The latter has not stirred. After a few seconds the child repeats his question a trifle louder, "Are you asleep?" and he adds, in the same expressionless, slightly singsong tone of voice, "You can't sleep here, you know."

The soldier has not stirred. The child might suppose he is alone in the room, merely pretending to have a conversation with someone who doesn't exist, or else with a doll, a toy unable to answer. Under these conditions it is certainly no use speaking louder; the voice in fact is that of a child telling himself a story.

But the voice is broken off, as if unable to struggle further against the silence which has prevailed again. The child, too, may have fallen asleep.

"No . . . Yes . . . I know," the soldier says.

Neither one has moved. The child is still standing in the half-darkness, his arms at his sides. He has not even seen the man's lips moving as he sits at the table under the one light bulb still lit in the room; the head has not moved at all, the eyes have not even blinked, and the mouth is still closed.

"Your father . . ." the soldier begins. Then he stops. But this time the lips have stirred a little.

"He's not my father," the child says.

And he turns his head toward the door with its black rectangle of window glass in the upper half.

It is snowing outside. Tiny flakes have begun falling again on the already white road. The wind has risen and is blowing them horizontally, so that the soldier has to keep his head down, a little further down, as he walks, pressing the hand shielding his eyes still harder against his forehead, leaving visible only a few square inches of thin, crunching snow that is already trampled down hard. Reaching a crossroads, the soldier hesitates and looks around for the plaques that should indicate the names of these streets. But it is useless, for there are no blue-enamel plaques here, or else they are set too high and the night is too dark; besides, the tiny, thick flakes quickly blind him when he tries to look up. Then too, a street name would hardly furnish him much in the way of helpful information: he doesn't know this city anyway.

He hesitates for another moment, looks ahead again, then back at the road he has just taken, with its row of street lamps whose circles of light, closer and closer together and less and less bright, soon disappear in the darkness. Then he turns right, onto the cross street which is also deserted, lined with the same kind of apartment houses and the same row of street lamps, quite far apart but set at regular intervals, their dim circles of light revealing the oblique snowfall as he passes each one.

The white flakes, falling thick and fast, suddenly change direction; vertical for a few seconds, they suddenly become almost horizontal. Then they are immobilized for an instant and begin, with a sudden gust of wind, to blow at virtually the same angle in the opposite direction, which they abandon after two or three seconds with no more transition than before, to return to their original orientation, making new, almost horizontal, parallel lines that cross the circle of light from left to right toward the unlighted windows.

In the window recesses the snow has formed an uneven layer, very shallow on the sill but deeper toward the back, making on the right side an already considerable drift, which fills the corner and reaches as high as the pane. All the ground-floor windows, one after the other, show exactly the same amount of snow which has drifted toward the right in the same way.

At the next crossroads, under the corner street lamp, a child is standing. He is partially hidden by the cast-iron post whose conical base conceals the lower part of his body altogether. He is watching the soldier approach. He does not seem bothered by the storm or by the snow that whitens some of his black cape and his beret. He is a boy of about ten, his expression serious.

He turns his head as the soldier comes toward him, following him with his eyes as he reaches the lamp post, then passes it. Since the soldier is not walking fast, the child has time to examine him carefully from head to foot: the unshaven cheeks, the apparent fatigue, the dirty and ragged overcoat, the sleeves without braid on them, the wet package under his left arm, both hands thrust deep in his pockets, the hurriedly wrapped, irregular leggings, the wide gash down the back of the right boot, at least six inches long and so deep it looks as if it pierces the leather; yet the boot is not split and the damaged area has merely been smeared with black wax, which now gives it the same dark-gray color as the adjoining surfaces that are still intact.

The man has stopped. Without moving the rest of his body, he has turned his head around toward the child looking at him, already some three steps away, already crosscrossed by many white lines.

A moment later the soldier slowly pivots around and makes a movement toward the street lamp. The boy steps back, against the cast-iron post; at the same time he draws tight the bottom of his cape, holding the cloth from inside without showing his hands. The man has stopped. Now that the gusts of snow are no longer striking him directly in the face, he can hold his head up without too much discomfort.

"Don't be afraid," he says.

He steps toward the child and repeats a little louder, "Don't be afraid."

The child does not answer. Without seeming to feel the thickset flakes that scarcely make him squint, he continues staring at the soldier directly in front of him. The latter begins:

"Do you know where . . ."

But goes no further. The question he was going to ask is not the right one. A gust of wind blows the snow into his face again. He takes his right hand out of his overcoat pocket and shields his eyes with it. He has no glove, his hand is red and dirty. When the gust is over he puts his hand back in his pocket.

"Where does this road go?"

The boy still says nothing. His eyes have left the soldier to look toward the end of the street in the direction the man has indicated with a nod of his head; he sees only the succession of street lamps, closer and closer together, less and less bright, which vanish into the darkness.

"What's the matter, are you afraid I'll eat you?"

"No," the child says. "I'm not afraid."

"Well then, tell me where this road goes."

"I don't know," the child says.

And he raises his eyes toward this ill-dressed, unshaven soldier who doesn't even know where he's going. Then, without warning, he makes a sudden turn, skillfully avoids the base of the lamp post and begins to run as fast as he can along the row of apartment houses, in the opposite direction from the way the soldier came. In a few seconds he has disappeared.

At the next street lamp he appears again for several seconds; he is still running just as fast; his cape billows out behind him. He reappears at each lamp post, once, twice, then no more.

The soldier turns back and continues on his way. Again the snow strikes him directly in the face.

He puts the package under his right arm to try to shield his face with his left hand, for the wind blows more continuously from this side. But he soons gives this up and quickly puts the hand, numb with cold, back in his overcoat pocket. Now he merely turns his head away to get less snow in his eyes, leaning toward the unlighted windows where the white drift continues to accumulate in the right-hand corner of the recess.

Yet this boy with the serious expression is the same boy who led him to the café run by the man who is not his father. And there was a similar scene under the same kind of lamp post, at an identical crossroads. Perhaps it was snowing a little less heavily. The flakes were thicker, heavier, slower. But the boy answered with just as much reticence, holding his black cape tight around his knees. He had the same serious expression and seemed to be just as untroubled by the snow. He hesitated just as long at each question before giving an answer which furnished his interlocutor no information. Where did the street go? A long silent stare toward the presumed end of the street, then the calm voice:

"To the boulevard."

"And this one?"

The boy slowly turns his eyes in the direction the man has just indicated with a nod of his head. His features reveal no difficulty remembering, no uncertainty when he repeats in the same expressionless tone:

"To the boulevard."

"The same one?"

Again there is silence, and the snow falling more and more slowly, heavily.

"Yes," the boy says. Then, after a pause, "No." And finally, with a sudden violence, "It's the boulevard!"

"And is it far?" the soldier asks again.

The child is still looking at the series of street lamps, closer and closer together, less and less bright, which here too vanish into the darkness.

"Yes," he says, his voice calm again and sounding as if it came from far away.

The soldier waits another minute to make sure there will not be another "no." But the boy is already running along the row of apartment houses, down the track of trampled snow the soldier followed in the opposite direction a few minutes earlier. When the running boy crosses a circle of light, his black cape billowing out behind him can be seen for a few seconds, once, twice, three times, smaller and vaguer at each reappearance, until there is nothing but a confused whirl of snow.

Yet it is certainly the same boy who walks ahead of the soldier when the latter comes to the café. Before crossing the doorstep, the child shakes his black cape and takes off his beret, which he knocks twice against the door jamb in order to brush off the bits of ice which have formed in the folds of the cloth. The soldier must have met him several times, while walking in circles through the maze of identical streets. He has never come to any boulevard, any broader road planted with trees or differing in any way at all from the other streets he has taken. Finally the child had spoken a few names, the few street names he knew, which were obviously of no use at all.

Now he is knocking his beret against the door jamb in front of which they both have stopped. The interior is brightly lit. A ruffled curtain of white, translucent material covers the lower part of the window set in the upper part of the door. But for a man of normal height it is easy to see the entire interior: the counter to the left, the tables in the middle, on the right a wall covered with posters of various sizes. There are few drinkers at this late hour: two workmen sitting at one of the tables and a man more carefully dressed standing near the zinc-topped counter over which the proprietor is leaning. The latter is a man of massive stature, whose size is even more noticeable in relation to his customer because of the slightly raised platform he is standing on. Both men have turned their heads toward the door where the boy has just knocked his beret against the jamb.

But they see only the soldier's face above the curtain. And the child turning the door knob with one hand, again knocks his beret, this time against the door itself, which is already some distance from the jamb. The proprietor's eyes have already left the soldier's pale face that is still silhouetted against the darkness, cut off at chin level by the curtain, and are lowered on the gap widening between door and jamb in order to let in the child.

As soon as he is inside, the latter turns around and gestures to the soldier to follow him. This time everyone stares at the newcomer: the proprietor behind his counter, the man standing in front of it, the two workmen sitting at a table. One of the latter, whose back was to the door, has pivoted on his chair without letting go his glass that is half full of red wine and set in the middle of the checkered tablecloth. The other glass, close beside the first, is also encircled by a large hand which completely conceals the probable contents. To the left, a ring of reddish liquid indicates another place where the same glass had been set down before.

Later, it is the soldier himself who is sitting in front of a similar glass, half full of the same dark-colored wine. On the red-and-white-checkered cloth the glass has left several circular marks, but almost all are incomplete, showing a series of more or less closed arcs, occasionally overlapping, almost dry in some places, in others still shiny with the last drops of liquid leaving a film over the blacker deposit already formed, while elsewhere the rings are blurred by being set too close together, or even half obliterated, perhaps, by a quick dab of a rag.

The soldier, motionless at the foot of his lamp post, is still waiting, his hands in his overcoat pockets, the same package under his left arm. It is daylight again, the same pale, colorless daylight. But the street lamp is out now. There are the same apartment houses, the same empty streets, the same gray-and-white hues, the same cold.

It has stopped snowing. The layer of snow on the ground is scarcely any deeper, perhaps only a little more solidly packed. And the yellowish paths the hurrying pedestrians have made along the sidewalks are just the same. On each side of these narrow paths the white surface has remained virtually intact; tiny changes have nevertheless occurred here and there, for instance the circular area which the soldier's heavy boots have stamped down near the lamp post.

It is the child who approaches him this time. At first he is only a vague silhouette, an irregular black spot coming closer quite fast along the outer edge of the sidewalk. Each time this spot passes a street lamp it makes a sudden movement toward it and immediately continues forward in its original direction. Soon it is easy to make out the agile legs in their narrow black trousers, the black cape billowing out over the shoulders, the beret pulled down over the boy's eyes. Each time the child passes a street lamp he stretches out his arm toward the cast-iron post which his wool-gloved hand grasps while his whole body, with the momentum of its accumulated speed, makes a complete turn around this pivot, his feet scarcely touching the ground until the child is back in his original position on the outer edge of the sidewalk where he continues running forward toward the soldier.

"Hello," the latter says.

The child looks at him without surprise, but also without the slightest indication of friendliness, as if he found it both natural and annoying to meet the soldier again.

"Where did you sleep?" he says finally.

The soldier makes a vague gesture with his chin, without bothering to take a hand out of his pocket. "Back there."

"In the barracks?"

"That's right, in the barracks."

The child examines his uniform from head to foot. The greenish overcoat is neither more nor less ragged, the leggings are just as carelessly wrapped, the boots have virtually the same mud stains. But the beard may be a little darker.

"Where is your barracks?"

"Back there," the soldier says. And he repeats the same gesture with his chin, pointing vaguely behind him, or over his right shoulder.

"You don't know how to wrap your leggings," the child says.

The man bends forward slightly and looks down toward his boots. "It doesn't matter any more now, you know."

As he straightens up again he notices that the boy is much closer than he expected him to be: only two or three yards away. He didn't recall that the child had stopped so close to him or if he had seen him come nearer afterwards. Still, it is hardly likely that the child has changed position without the soldier's knowing it, while the latter's head was down: in so short an interval of time he would scarcely have been able to take a step. Besides, he is standing in exactly the same position as at the beginning of their encounter: body rigid in the black cape held shut—even tight, around the body—by his invisible hands, eyes raised.

"Twelve thousand three hundred forty-five," the child says, reading off the regiment number on the coat collar.

"Yes," the soldier says. "But that isn't my number."

"Yes it is. It's written on you."

"But now, you know . . ."

"It's even written twice." And the child sticks one arm out from under his cape and points his index finger toward two red tabs. He is wearing a navy-blue sweater and a knitted wool glove of the same color.

"All right . . . if you say so," the soldier says.

The child puts his arm back under the cape, which he carefully closes again, holding it tight from inside.

"What's in that package?"

"I've already told you."

Suddenly the child turns his head toward the door of the apartment building. Thinking he has seen something strange there, the soldier turns to look too, but sees only the same vertical dark opening, a hand's width across, separating the door from the jamb. Since the boy is still looking attentively in this direction, the man tries to discern some figure in the shadowy entrance, but with no success.

Finally he asks, "What are you looking at?"

"What's in that package?" the child repeats instead of answering, still not looking away from the open door.

"I've already told you: some stuff."

"What stuff?"

"My stuff!"

The boy looks up toward his interlocutor:

"You have a sack to keep your stuff in. Every soldier has a sack."

He has become increasingly self-assured during the conversation. His voice is now not at all remote, but firm, almost peremptory. The man, on the other hand, is speaking lower and lower:

"It's all over, you know, now. The war's over . . ."

Again he feels how tired he is. He doesn't want to answer any more questions that lead nowhere. A little more of this and he'll give the boy the package. He looks at the box in its brown wrapping paper under his arm; in drying, the snow has left dark rings on it, their edges fringed with tiny scallops; half undone, the string around the package has slipped toward the corners.

Beyond the boy, who is still standing there, the soldier looks down the empty street. Turning toward the opposite end, he sees the same shallow perspective.

"Don't you know what time it is?" he asks, resuming his initial position against the cast-iron post.

The boy shakes his head several times, from left to right, from right to left.

"Does your father serve meals?"

"He's not my father," the child says; and, without giving the man time to ask his question again, he turns on his heel and walks stiffly toward the half-open door. He stops on the doorstep, pushes the door a little further open, slips into the opening and closes the door behind him without slamming it but so that the click of the bolt falling into place can be clearly heard.

The soldier no longer sees anything in front of him now but the snow-covered sidewalk with its yellowish path on the right-hand side and, to the left, a smooth surface broken by a single regular path: a series of small footprints running parallel to the gutter, then, about four yards from the lamp post, coming together at a place where the snow is more heavily trampled and turning at right angles to join the narrower path leading to the apartment-house door.

The soldier raises his face toward the gray façade with its rows of uniform windows, a white streak along the bottom of each recess, perhaps supposing he will see the boy appear at one of the windows. But he knows that the child in the cape does not live in this house, for he has already gone with him to where he lives. Besides, judging from the look of the windows, the whole apartment building is unoccupied.

In the picture, the child is sitting on the floor with his legs folded under him; it looks as if he wanted to slide all the way under the bench. But he continues to look straight ahead, his attentiveness indicated more by his wide-open eyes than anything else.

This sign, of course, is not infallible; if the artist had meant the child to be looking at nothing in particular, if he had imagined no specific feature for the fourth wall of this rectangular room where only three are shown, it could be said that the child is merely staring into space. But, if this were the case, it was unsuitable to represent him staring at the only one of the four walls that apparently opens out onto something. The three walls shown in the print have, as a matter of fact, no visible opening in them. Even if there were an exit at the left, behind the coat racks, it is certainly not the main entrance to the tavern, for if it were, the present arrangement of tables and counter would be too inconvenient. The main entrance, with white enamel letters spelling out the word "Café" and the proprietor's name in two curved lines pasted on the glass in the form of an oval, and below this a ruffled curtain of thin, translucent material, obliging anyone who wants to look over it to stand close against the door—this main door must be in the wall that is not shown in the print, the rest of this wall being taken up by a large window, also with a long curtain covering its lower half and decorated in the middle by three spheres attached to the glass—one red one above two white ones—suggesting that the exit behind the coat-racks leads to a billiard parlor.

The child holding the box in his arms would therefore be looking toward the door, but he is sitting almost at floor level and obviously cannot see the street over the curtain. He is not looking up as if at some pale face pressed against the glass cut off at neck level by the curtain. His gaze is virtually horizontal. Has the door just been opened to let in some newcomer who attracts the boy's attention by his unusual uniform: a soldier, for instance? This seems unlikely, for ordinarily the main entrance is next to the counter—that is, in this case, on the far left, where there is a small cleared space in front of the standing men dressed as burghers. The child, though, is sitting on the right-hand side of the picture, where no passage among the jumble of benches and tables permits access to the rest of the taproom.

The soldier, moreover, has been in the room for a long time. He is sitting at a table far behind the child, who does not seem at all interested in his uniform. The soldier is also looking straight ahead, his eyes slightly raised; but since he is much further away from the window than the boy, he need only raise his eyes a few degrees to look through the window above the curtain at the snow falling thick and fast, again obliterating the footprints, the tracks made by isolated steps, the yellowish crisscrossed paths parallel to the high façades.

At the corner of the last apartment house, standing in the

L-shaped strip of snow between the latter and the path, one foot, one leg, one shoulder and half the black cape out of sight, the boy is on the lookout, his eyes fixed on the cast-iron lamp post. Has he come out of the apartment by another door opening on the cross street, or has he stepped through a ground-floor window? In either case, the soldier pretends not to have noticed his reappearance. Leaning against his street lamp, he appears absorbed in examining the deserted roadway at the far end of the street.

"What are you waiting for?" Then, in the same tone of voice, after ten seconds, "What are you waiting for there?"

The voice is certainly the boy's, the tone deliberate, calm and without friendliness, a little too deep for a boy of ten or twelve. But it sounds quite close, scarcely two or three yards away, whereas the corner of the building is at least eight yards off. The man feels like turning around to verify this distance and seeing if the child has not come closer again. Or else, without looking at him, he may answer his question with the first thing that comes into his head: "The streetcar," or "Christmas," to make the child understand what a bother he is. The soldier continues to stare down the street.

When he finally turns to look at the boy, the latter has disappeared altogether. The soldier waits another minute, thinking the boy has only stepped behind the cornice and will soon peek out from behind his hiding place. But no such thing happens.

The man looks down at the smooth snow, where the newly made footprints turn at right angles just in front of him. In the section parallel to the sidewalk the footprints are wide apart and smudged by running, a tiny heap of snow having been thrown up behind each one by the movement of the shoes; on the other hand, the few steps leading to the path show the pattern of the soles very clearly: a series of chevrons across the width of the sole and, beneath the heel, a cross inscribed in a circle— that is, on the heel itself, a cross inscribed in a circular de-pression in the rubber (a second round hole, much shallower and of extremely small diameter, may indicate the center of the cross, with the shoe size shown by figures in relief: thirty-two, perhaps thirty-three or thirty-four).

The soldier, who had bent over slightly to examine the details of the footprints, then walks to the path. As he passes it he tries to push open the apartment-house door, but the latter resists: it is shut tight. It is a wooden door with ornamental moldings, with extremely narrow jambs on either side. The man continues walking toward the corner of the building and turns down the cross street, which is as empty as the one he has just left.

The cross street, like the other, leads to a right-angle cross-roads with a final street lamp set some ten yards before the end of the sidewalk and identical façades on each side. The base of the cast-iron lamp post is a truncated cone embossed with a strand of ivy, with the same curves, the same leaves growing at the same places on the same stems, the same faults in the casting. The entire design is accentuated by the same borders of snow. Perhaps the meeting was supposed to be at this crossroads.

The soldier raises his eyes to look for the enamel plaques which should show the names of these streets. There is nothing visible on one of the stone walls at the corner. On the other, about three yards above the ground, is attached the standard blue plaque from which the enamel has chipped off in large flakes, as if boys had taken it as a target for throwing pebbles; only the word "Rue" is still legible and, further on, the two letters: ". . . na . . ." followed by a downstroke interrupted by the concentric rings of the next chip. The name must have been an extremely short one. The depredations are quite old, for the exposed metal is already badly rusted.

As he is about to cross the street, still following the thin yellow path, to see if he cannot find other street signs in better condition, the man hears a voice quite nearby, which pronounces three or four syllables whose sense he has not time to grasp.

He immediately turns around; but there is no one in sight. In this solitude, the snow probably conducts sound strangely.

The voice was low and yet it did not sound like a man's voice. . . . A young woman with an extremely low voice—that may have been what it was, but the recollection is too fugitive: already nothing remains but a neutral timbre, without any particular tone; it could belong to anyone, might not even be a human voice at all. At this moment the soldier notices that the corner apartment-house door is not closed. He takes a few steps toward it. The interior is so dark that it is impossible to see anything. To the right, to the left, up above, all the windows are closed, their dirty black panes without curtains or shades suggesting no trace of life in the unlighted rooms, as if the entire building were deserted.

The wooden door has ornamental moldings and is painted dark brown; on either side are the narrow jambs. The soldier pushes the door wide open as he steps up onto the snow-covered stoop which already shows many footprints, and steps inside.

He is standing at the end of a dark corridor with several doors opening off it. At the other end he can discern a staircase rising out of the corridor and soon vanishing in the darkness. The other end of this long, narrow entranceway also opens onto another hallway perpendicular to the first, marked by even darker shadows on each side of the staircase. The corridor is empty, without any of those domestic objects that generally reveal the life of a house: doormats in front of the doors, toys left at the foot of the stairs, bucket and mop leaning against a corner. Here there is nothing, except the floor and the walls; and even the walls are bare, all painted some very dark color; just to the left of the entrance is tacked the little white sign instructing the residents what to do in case of fire. The floor is of ordinary wood blackened by mud and slops, as are the first steps—the only ones clearly visible—of the staircase. After five or six steps the staircase seems to turn to the right. The soldier can now make out the wall behind the stairs. Here, as close to the wall as possible, her arms held rigid alongside her body, is standing a woman in a full skirt and a long apron tied around her waist; she is staring at the open entrance door and the figure standing there silhouetted against the light.

Before the man has had time to speak a word to her, a door on the left-hand side of the corridor suddenly opens, and another woman in an apron, heavier-set than the first and perhaps older too, steps out. Looking up, she stops short, opens her mouth wide—too wide—and as she steps back into the doorway begins to scream, the shrill sound rising until it ends in the violent slamming of her door. At the same moment comes the sound of hurried steps going up the staircase; it is the other woman running away, vanishing at once, though the pounding of her clogs continues as she ascends without any lessening of speed, the sound fading from floor to floor as she climbs, her full skirt which she holds down with one hand billowing around her legs while she doesn't even stop on the landings to catch her breath, the only clue as to her position being suggested by a different resonance at the beginning and the end of each flight: one floor, two floors, three or four floors, even more.

Afterwards there is complete silence again. But, on the right-hand side of the corridor this time, another door has opened. Or was it already open before? It is more likely that the sudden racket has just attracted this new figure, which resembles the preceding two, or at least the first: a woman, also young, apparently, and wearing a long dark-gray apron tied around her waist and hanging loosely over her hips. Her eyes meeting the soldier's, she asks:

"What's going on here?"

Her voice is low and deep, but with a premeditated quality about it, as if she wanted to sound as impersonal as possible. This might also be the voice heard in the street a moment ago.

"They got scared," the soldier says.

"Yes," the woman says, "it's from seeing you standing there like that . . . with the light behind you . . . they can't see . . . they thought you were a . . ."

She does not finish her sentence. She stands still, staring at him. She opens her door no wider, probably feeling safer inside, holding the door in one hand and resting her other on the jamb, ready to close it again. She asks:

"What do you want?"

"I'm looking for a street . . ." the soldier says, "a street I have to go to."

"What street?"

"That's just it, I can't remember the name. It was something like Galavier, or Matabier. But I'm not sure. Could it be Montoret?"

The woman seems to be thinking.

"This is a big city, you know," she says at last.

"But it's around here somewhere, that's what they told me."

The young woman turns her head toward the interior of the apartment and in a louder voice questions someone who remains invisible, "Did you ever hear of a Rue Montoret? Somewhere around here? Or something that sounds like that?"

She waits for the answer, her regular profile appearing as she turns toward the opening of the door. Everything behind her is dark: there must be a hallway without any windows. The fat woman also came out of complete darkness. After a moment a faint voice answers a few indistinct words, and the young woman turns back toward the soldier:

"Wait here a minute. I'll go see."

She begins to close the door, then changes her mind. "Close the street door," she says, "the whole house is getting cold."

The soldier walks back to the door and pushes it shut, the bolt making a faint click as it falls into place. He is in the dark again. The woman must have closed her door too. It is not even possible to walk toward it, for he has no means of getting his bearings, not even a gleam of light. Complete darkness. Nor can he hear the slightest sound: neither steps nor murmurs nor the clatter of kitchen utensils. The whole house seems uninhabited. The soldier closes his eyes and sees again the white flakes slowly falling, the row of street lamps set at regular intervals from one end of the snow-covered sidewalk to the other, and the boy running away as fast as he can, appearing every few seconds in the successive circles of light, and, though the time intervals are the same, the space covered is foreshortened, so that the boy seems to be running slower and slower as he grows smaller and smaller.

Le Jardin

––––––––––

by YVES BONNEFOY

––––––––––

Tu cesses de venir dans ce jardin,
Les chemins de souffrir et d'être seul s'effacent,
Les herbes signifient ton visage mort.

Il ne t'importe plus que soient cachés
Dans la pierre l'église obscure, dans les arbres
Le visage aveuglé d'un plus rouge soleil,

Il te suffit
De mourir longuement comme en sommeil,
Tu n'aimes même plus l'ombre que tu épouses.

English Translation

by D'ELBERT E. KEENAN

So you no longer come back to this garden,
The roads of suffering and loneliness fade out,
Weeds grow to signify your lifeless face.

You care no longer now that here are hidden
The dark church in the stone, and in the trees
The face that's blinded by a redder sun.

It is enough
For you to die a long death as in sleep,
You no longer even love the shade you wed.

Tiberius, a play*

---

by FÉLICIEN MARCEAU

English version by RICHARD HOWARD

CAST OF CHARACTERS

ANNOUNCER

TIBERIUS

CORNELIUS, HIS SECRETARY

LIVIA, A YOUNG SLAVE

AETIUS, A YOUNG SLAVE

JULIA

THE DEAF MAN

OVIDIUS NASO

TIBERIUS' FATHER

TIBERIUS' MOTHER

TIBERIUS AS A CHILD

CASSIUS

AUGUSTUS

A LOUD VOICE

THE TOURISTS

FIRST VOICE, *a man*
SECOND VOICE, *a woman*
THIRD VOICE, *a man*
FOURTH VOICE, *a woman*
FIFTH VOICE, *a man*
CHARLES
EIGHTH VOICE, *a woman*
TWENTY-FIRST VOICE, *a woman*

CHAUFFEURS, HOTEL PORTERS, GUIDES, ETC.

SIXTH VOICE, *a man*
SEVENTH VOICE, *a man*
NINTH VOICE, *a man*
TENTH VOICE, *a man*
SEVENTEENTH VOICE, *a man*
A GUIDE
FIRST PROFESSOR
SECOND PROFESSOR

HABITUÉS OF CAPRI

ELEVENTH VOICE, *a woman*
TWELFTH VOICE, *a man*
THIRTEENTH VOICE, *a woman*
FOURTEENTH VOICE, *a man*
FIFTEENTH VOICE, *a man*
SIXTEENTH VOICE, *a woman*
EIGHTEENTH VOICE, *a woman*
NINETEENTH VOICE, *a woman*
TWENTIETH VOICE, *a man*

An effort should be made, with regard to the tourists and the habitués, to use a different general tone: for the tourists, amazement; for the habitués, boredom.

[*At top volume, a Neapolitan tune* "Funiculi-Funicula" *or* "O Sole Mio"; *first with the words, then nothing but the music, under which we can hear the regular beat of a ship's engine and the babble of conversation in several languages.*]

FIRST VOICE, *a man.* Magnifico!

SECOND VOICE, *a woman.* Ah, que c'est belle!

THIRD VOICE, *a man.* Schön! Wunderbar!

FOURTH VOICE, *a woman.* Look at that, Charles! It's like a dream!

FIFTH VOICE, *a man.* Skönhetens o!

ANNOUNCER. Ladies and gentlemen, my microphone and I are on board the ship taking passengers from Naples to Capri. It is a beautiful day and a charming moment, only a trifle spoiled, perhaps, by the ship's phonograph. The sun is shining, the air is transparent, and the sea incredibly blue. As blue as the bluest eyes. As for the boat, it certainly is . . . a boat all right. Big, clean and white too: like boats of this kind all over the world. Behind us lies the Bay of Naples, Mount Vesuvius, with its cone: truncated—for the moment; the headland of Sorrento, and Cape Messina. Ahead of us lies the island; perhaps the most famous island in the world, the Island of Capri. At this very moment we are approaching the harbor. Directly above us are the ruins of the Emperor Tiberius' palace.

FOURTH VOICE. Just look at that, Charles! That's supposed to be where he had his slaves thrown into the sea.

CHARLES [*impressed*]. You don't mean it!

ANNOUNCER. Now we're passing alongside high cliffs, rose-color and ochre, crowned with palm trees and cactuses. Here's where the ship turns. . . . [*Two blasts of the boat whistle.*] Pink houses, red houses, blue houses and even white ones. Bright blue and faded blue. A swarm of balconies, porches, archways and down below the fishing smacks, the pier, boys running barefoot down to the boat, high above us the campanile with its great clock. Now the gangplank is coming out. . . . [*Muffled sound of the gangplank. The music has stopped.*] The porters have come on board, and down on the pier stand the hotel chauffeurs, their hats. . . .

SIXTH VOICE, *a man.* Hotel Quisisana! Hotel Quisisana!

SEVENTH VOICE, *a man* [*Italian accent*]. Blue grotto, Lady, blue grotto, very pretty!

EIGHTH VOICE, *a woman* [*hysterical*]. *Facchino! Facchino!*

NINTH VOICE, *a man. Albergo le Palme!*

TENTH VOICE, *a man. Carozella?* Pretty ride, no take much money.

ANNOUNCER. No, no *carozella.* Like everyone else, we'll take the funicular, the little red car that goes all the way to the top. [*Sound of a whistle and the funicular machinery.*] Valiantly, the little red car climbs up and up, between the vines, the geraniums and the roses. Here we are at the piazza.

[*The babble grows louder.*]

EIGHTH VOICE [*hysterical*]. *Facchino!* Where is my luggage?

ANNOUNCER. Now, here we are *in* the piazza. Capri's piazza has nothing in common with the Place de la Concorde or Times Square; it's nothing like those great windy stretches with streets running into them like rivers. In Capri, the piazza is very small, and closed in on all sides. Like a room, if you can imagine it, or like a stage set. Yes, a stage set, that's the word I was looking for. A stage set where the play calls for a lot of chairs, for instance. There are three cafés. Each one overflows the sidewalk, setting up its tables and chairs and bright umbrellas wherever it can. There's hardly any room to walk. And wherever you look, a fantastic crowd—fantastic is hardly the word—here nobody would be surprised to see a man in red shorts or an elderly lady in flowered toreador pants.

FOURTH VOICE. Charles, just look at that hat!

CHARLES. You don't say!

FOURTH VOICE. And look at that man over there! The one with the gold chain.

CHARLES. Certainly is a type.

ELEVENTH VOICE, *a woman, Comment allez-vous?*

TWELFTH VOICE, *a man. Ma chi si vede?*

THIRTEENTH VOICE, *a woman.* What a delightful surprise!

FOURTEENTH VOICE, *a man [bored tone]. Comment allez-vous?*

FIFTEENTH VOICE, *a man. Ach so!*

SIXTEENTH VOICE, *a woman.* What'll we do today?

SEVENTEENTH VOICE, *a man.* Postcards, jewelry, souvenirs. . . .

FOURTEENTH VOICE [*increasingly bored*]. *Comment allez-vous?*

EIGHTEENTH VOICE, *a woman [yawning].* I think I'll go back to the hotel and take a nap.

CHARLES. You don't say!

NINETEENTH VOICE, *a woman.* She's supposed to be with Bobby now.

TWENTIETH VOICE, *a man.* Oh no, she's not; I saw her with Toto last night!

FOURTEENTH VOICE [*exhausted*]. *Comment allez-vous?*

ANNOUNCER. Good heavens! They don't seem to be having as much fun as their red shorts would indicate. Let's take this alley, the one that turns off here under an archway. . . . [*The babble dies away*]. Shops, more shops . . . the alley continues. Now we are walking along between gray walls, a gray as old as time. . . . Every once in a while you see a lizard, as quick as a whiplash. . . . Now you can breathe, there are no more houses here. Can you smell the lavender? It grows wild here. The alley has turned into a path, and the path climbs up. Cactus and euphorbia. . . . And here at last is the palace of Tiberius! Of Tiberius, ladies and gentlemen! Or rather its ruins. Enormous, inhuman ruins, gaping halls, cellars, giant staircases, columns lying in the grass. Here, then is the place where Tiberius chose to live, far from all mankind. Here, almost as he saw it, is the landscape that lay before his eyes. Virtually nothing has changed. Down below, the sea. . . . Opposite, so clear you could almost reach out and touch it, the hills of the continent—Italy. The blue line of the mountains, the headland of Sorrento like a Sphinx with its great paws resting on the sea.

FOURTH VOICE. Look at that, Charles! It's where he lived for years and years.

CHARLES. He might have chosen worse.

ANNOUNCER. Tiberius. . . . Who was Tiberius? Who was this strange emperor who chose to live three hundred miles from his capital and, in a manner of speaking, on vacation from power? Why this retreat? Why this disgust? Was Tiberius a philosopher, a pessimist despising mankind and seeking refuge here in order to escape them?

FOURTH VOICE. They say he had all kinds of goings-on here: orgies, debauches. . . . This palace must have seen everything.

CHARLES. If only the walls could talk!

A GUIDE. Notice this narrow ledge. Be careful, *Signora:* watch your little girl. According to tradition, this is where Tiberius had his slaves hurled into the sea. If you lean over, you can see how far they fell. The wretched bodies were crushed on the rocks below. [*Tragically*] They were corpses when they reached the bottom.

TWENTY-FIRST VOICE, *a woman. Terribile!*

FOURTH VOICE. Charles, hold my arm!

ANNOUNCER. Or was it himself Tiberius despised? Did he feel somehow unworthy of his position, unworthy to rule, perhaps unworthy to live? Horror-stricken before the monster his mirror showed him? Perhaps he took refuge here only to conceal his shame and his vices at the same time! Who knows why he came to Capri—perhaps he sought this dreadful freedom from power merely to be himself. To be nothing but the monster that he was, without constraint, without limitation, without any witnesses save his accomplices.

FIRST PROFESSOR. Read Suetonius—Tiberius was a cunning scoundrel!

SECOND PROFESSOR. Read Tacitus—Tiberius was a bad emperor and a terrible master as well—cruel, vindictive and underhanded.

FIRST PROFESSOR. What's more, he drank. They even nicknamed him Biberius: that says a lot.

SECOND PROFESSOR. And lustful, perverse. . . . They also nicknamed him Caprineus, which means both an inhabitant of Capri and an old goat.

ANNOUNCER. It's true that both Suetonius and Tacitus heaped abuse on Tiberius. Yet Paterculus eulogized him.

FIRST PROFESSOR [disdainfully]. Oh, Paterculus!

ANNOUNCER. I know. No one reads Paterculus any more. Tacitus and Suetonius had talent; Paterculus none. But what must we think of history, gentlemen, if its verdicts depend solely on the talent of the historians who happened to be on the spot? What would we think of Napoleon if we had to judge him only by Chateaubriand?

SECOND PROFESSOR. Nevertheless, the texts speak for themselves.

ANNOUNCER. And they contain a number of curious contradictions, too. One day Tiberius has a grammarian thrown into prison because he disagrees with him about where a comma belongs. Perhaps this was not exactly a generous characteristic. But another day this same Tiberius asks forgiveness from every patient in a hospital because they have all been moved from their beds in honor of his visit. Certainly this gives evidence of a more delicate sensibility.

FIRST PROFESSOR. History has condemned him.

ANNOUNCER. Not without a few dissenting voices. Mommsen,

a serious historian if there ever was one, assures us Tiberius
was the most capable emperor Rome ever knew.

SECOND PROFESSOR. Rome didn't know him very well: he was
never there!

ANNOUNCER. Perhaps he had invented an original form of government: power by remote control, power abstracted. . . .
It was a new idea!

FOURTH VOICE. As far as I'm concerned, Charles, your Tiberius
was a disgusting old man.

CHARLES. He's not *my* Tiberius. . . .

ANNOUNCER. But what if Tiberius was none of these things.
Supposing Tiberius were nothing but a lonely old man? An
emperor of course, a Roman emperor—and right away we
start imagining things, a certain stature, a style. . . . But
out of all those emperors there certainly must have been some
who were just ordinary old men. [*Sound of a zither and a
fountain.*]

*   *   *

Ladies and gentlemen, I have a man here with me, a man
wearing a tunic, and playing a zither as well. Perhaps you
can hear a fountain too, like a dove cooing—can you guess?
Yes, ladies and gentlemen, this old man, this great head, this
face covered with sores, these eyes, this sullen, blasé expression . . . Tiberius. . . .

TIBERIUS. The same.

FOURTH VOICE. Charles, look at him! He looks just like Mr.
Chamberlain!

ANNOUNCER [*enthusiastically*]. A miracle of science! A triumph
of technology! The presence of man projected, prolonged in
the places he has loved. What is time but a shadow? Twenty
centuries have vanished as if they had never been, like a
stone falling into a well. Ladies and gentlemen, I stand here
before Tiberius, the Emperor Tiberius himself, in flesh and

blood. Tiberius, one question, only one. Tiberius, *who were you;* what kind of man were you; what is your secret?

TIBERIUS. Century after century, your question has haunted me, asked by many lips. Was there so much about me, after all, to trouble men? Am I so bizarre? Tiberius . . . who was Tiberius? Do I know myself? Does anyone know who he is? Do you? Do you know who you are? Between us and the truth of ourselves lie too many mirrors, too many actions committed without knowing why. . . . Without any reason. Because we were bored or absent-minded. One forgets everything. The truth has no place left to stand; the truth . . . the truth has turned her ankle.

ANNOUNCER. But even so . . . you must have asked yourself questions every now and then . . .

TIBERIUS. I'll tell you. Perhaps I'm only a man who has been bored his whole life long—because he bored himself, that's all. That's probably what no one has ever forgiven me for, century after century: for being bored and not having the prudence, the modesty to conceal it. Everyone else pretends. I never pretended: that is my crime. Men need to believe in life—need to believe that it's, oh, that it's so important, so complicated—that it's worth taking the trouble to upset yourself, ask yourself questions, find answers—even principles. They get excited—they make desperate efforts. So, when someone doesn't do the same thing, when someone yawns— what can you expect? They turn furious. How can you believe in life when someone beside you is yawning? And an emperor into the bargain! A man whose yawn, you know, covers so much ground. A yawning emperor is the earth itself beginning to doubt.

ANNOUNCER. Perhaps this was due to some deficiency on your part?

TIBERIUS. That's it. That's mankind's great discovery. You tell them love is a fiction and they answer: it's your own heart that's a vacuum. You tell them power is delusion and they reply: it's your own head that's a void. You tell them the world is nothing but appearances, surfaces, shadows . . . and they complain: you haven't understood! That's why you can't escape any more; that's why you can never escape—why the truth always evades you. Because no one dares speak out— because no one dares say—nothing's there . . . nothing! And everyone goes on pretending. But what is life, after all? If, to begin with, you have to provide everything yourself— your heart, your head, and your lies? And what if that were it? What if that were the secret: that life is nothing; that man is a kind of bug—barely visible on the crust of the world. What if there were nothing to look for, nothing to understand. Here, young man, you with your hand on your heart, you with your twenty centuries' advantage over me, can you honestly assure me that life is worth the trouble?

ANNOUNCER. It seems to me . . .

TIBERIUS. "It seems to me" . . . you see, you're not even sure. . . . Let me put it this way: if life were really all that marvelous—the unique, irreplaceable thing men say it is— imagine how vindictive I would be about it! To me life has given nothing but boredom. . . . Vindictiveness, you know, is one of the words they hit upon to define me.

ANNOUNCER. "Tiberius, the resentful." I seem to remember something that sounded like that.

TIBERIUS. All because of a few retaliations . . . somewhat postponed—as if I postponed them of my own accord. All right, young man, you have a choice of two alternatives. Either I'm right: life is nothing; or else it's something, and in that case, you must tell me why I've been neglected by it. Why has life given me nothing—nothing, not one sigh, not one heartbeat?

ANNOUNCER. Perhaps you haven't known how to take it.

TIBERIUS. Then there was something to take?

ANNOUNCER. A destiny like yours. . . .

TIBERIUS. Oh, you too? I'm always hearing that. Everyone supposes I've been spoiled by life. Well, if I have, at least I haven't noticed it. Was I impotent? That was one explanation provided for me, you know. Very kind, but it doesn't explain a thing. My life . . . here, this is Cornelius, my secretary. . . .

ANNOUNCER. Pleased to meet you.

TIBERIUS. We don't have much to do on the island. . . . The days are rather empty. I've given Cornelius the job of putting together some notes for my biography. In the evening he reads them back to me or else I have my slaves act out some scenes from my life. I still entertain a vague hope that, by looking in the mirror they hold up for me, I'll finally discover something. Something strange, something interesting. A sentence I might not have noticed at the time. An episode when my heart should have beat a little faster. But I don't find anything. Nothing, Nothing. Everything is dim, gray, ridiculous. That's been my whole life. Would you like to see for yourself? Show him, Cornelius, show him. Tell him my life.

CORNELIUS. Where shall I begin?

TIBERIUS. At the beginning.

CORNELIUS. You were born forty-two years before the birth of Jesus Christ—I'm using the new style of reckoning.

TIBERIUS. It doesn't matter. For all the use we make of them, one date is as good as another.

ANNOUNCER. Surely you can't. . . .

TIBERIUS. Figures are only figures. Unless you mean money or soldiers, there's nothing behind them.

CORNELIUS. Your family——

TIBERIUS. It doesn't matter.

CORNELIUS. —was an extremely ancient family.

TIBERIUS. Too ancient. It left me nothing but its exhaustion.

CORNELIUS. It has included several interesting personalities.

TIBERIUS. Bah! People give themselves airs. Illusions. In every family, there's always an eccentric uncle or an old-maid aunt who wears last year's dresses and electrifies dinner parties by occasionally telling the truth. I suppose you believe in heredity? All that hodge-podge we're supposedly made from? My family was like every family: a jumble, a chaos of sages and imbeciles, honest merchants and pirates, watchful virgins and tirelessly adulterous wives. What help can you find in that? If there's a saying, "like father like son"; there's another—"miserly father spendthrift son." Those are the august laws of heredity for you.

CORNELIUS. Speaking of fathers, your own, Tiberius Nero——

TIBERIUS. You need not stop over that. My father was quaestor, admiral and governor, one after the other. He passed from each office to the next, and beneath all those uniforms never had the time to be himself.

ANNOUNCER. You see! Didn't I say there was some deficiency on your part? Anyone else would have tried to find out what was under that uniform.

TIBERIUS. There was nothing at all; I'd swear to that. Unless you're very careful, being an official is a way of being eaten: after a few years you're nothing but your job—a soldier, a sailor, a governor. . . .

CORNELIUS. There is, however, one singular action of your father's to remark: he surrendered his wife to the Emperor Augustus.

TIBERIUS. Just what I was saying! The official in him had devoured the husband. He no longer thought of anything except his promotion. The day came when promotion depended on giving up his wife. He didn't hesitate.

CORNELIUS. Previously, he had known disgrace. He had been forced to flee the country, go into hiding. You had just been born. One night, he and your mother were wandering quite

near by—in the outskirts of Naples, as a matter of fact—
pursued by soldiers and trying to get passage on a ship. You
were crying; your screams almost betrayed him.

[*sound of a child crying.*]

TIBERIUS' FATHER. Make him be quiet; the soldiers will hear
us!

TIBERIUS' MOTHER. There, there, darling, be still now, be still.

TIBERIUS. And to think I've actually been reproached for not
wanting to raise my voice! Ever since childhood I've been
told to be still. Obviously I had found my vocation, though:
I love silence.

CORNELIUS. Your father died. At the age of nine, you pro-
nounced his funeral oration. The speech was widely remarked
upon.

VOICE OF TIBERIUS AS A CHILD. Citizens, the man we have
lately lost was the model of every virtue.

TIBERIUS. Nonsense! What does all that have to do with me?
A speech I learned by heart, a speech my tutor drummed
into me fifty times over! And I didn't understand one word
of it. And yet that's the sort of thing they make biographies
out of. Out of what resembles us the least. I was a silent little
boy, afraid to raise his voice. And what is the one thing that
is remembered about that little boy? A speech. . . . Come
here, boy. . . . Now could I have ever been this child?
Could I have had these wide eyes, these freckles over my
nose, this shock of hair hanging into my face? Incredible!
What is the slow corruption that has turned this child into
the man I am—this obese old man, dreaming. . . . How
strange it all is! A child! . . . Something that scarcely weighs
upon the earth: something that plays, that hops on one leg
as if to weigh still less. And yet one day becomes a man, a
man who kills, who puts his big feet everywhere, who casts
a shadow . . . who becomes an emperor? Nonsense! Have
you ever thought about it? The fate of the world, government,

business, prefectures, *everything* is entrusted to former children! And you think I should take life seriously?

CORNELIUS. At the age of twenty-three, you married Vipsania, also called Agrippina, daughter of Agrippa.

TIBERIUS. [*growing animated*]. Ah! Now it's becoming interesting. We'll act this out. Aetius, you play my part. No boy, no, stand up straight. A little bearing there! A little— It's strange having someone else act out your life. . . . Did you ever make the experiment?

ANNOUNCER. No, as a matter of fact; I've never had occasion to.

TIBERIUS. You watch yourself, but you don't recognize anything. Then you make corrections; you *retouch*. Where's that big blond girl we had playing Vipsania the other night?

LIVIA. Here, my lord.

TIBERIUS. What's your name again?

LIVIA. Livia, my lord.

TIBERIUS. All right. You'll be Vipsania, the wife of Tiberius. I remember how gentle she was. . . . You have to have a certain majesty—not too much; and above all—be slow. On stage! The scene is my house in Rome: columns, couches, a garden in the background and beyond, the Coliseum. I am returning from the Senate. Vipsania is waiting for me. That was what was so marvelous about Vipsania, she was always waiting. Sometimes I would come home early, thinking I might surprise her at some household diversion. But I never did. She was always waiting for me. All right, begin.

LIVIA, *as Vipsania*. Did you have a good day?

AETIUS, *as Tiberius*. Exhausting!

LIVIA. Again?

AETIUS. What do you mean, "again"?

LIVIA. You were tired when you came home yesterday, too.

AETIUS. Rome wears me out. All this noise, all this commotion—all these men on the prowl or lying in wait, all these shifty eyes and all these open hands! There's something in modern life that extinguishes me, Vipsania. And as for the Senate! Either I have to listen to all the others talk, and every bone in my face cracks from yawning, or else I have to talk myself and that's even worse. My own singsong puts me to sleep.

LIVIA. Did you speak today?

AETIUS. Well, I had promised to; I let them trap me again. It's so much easier to promise than to refuse. The only trouble with promises is that you have to keep them. I was supposed to make a speech about the inhabitants of Laodicea. They've had an earthquake. I don't know why I should have to talk about it—an earthquake is the kind of idea anyone can understand. You'd think it would be enough just to say, "There was an earthquake in Laodicea. It wasn't anyone's fault, but there were damages. Let's vote subsidies." But you can't. With our Senators, you have to go into detail, find certain accents, a catch in your throat to describe houses falling, cracks opening in the earth, the dust, the dead, the viaducts, the wounded, the widows, and the orphans. I feel as if I had had that earthquake on my back all day.

LIVIA. Poor Tiberius! Rest now.

AETIUS. Ah, Vipsania, I'm all right when I'm with you. I feel happy now. Sweet Vipsania, calm Vipsania. . . .

ANNOUNCER. Did you love her?

TIBERIUS. If love is peace, if love is rest—yes, I loved her. In her presence I found that infinite sweetness that comes, not from living, but from leaving off. . . . I stopped living, with Vipsania. She never spoke one word louder than any other. Her disposition was smoother than a pond. She dozed and, beside her, I dozed too. That was happiness.

CORNELIUS. Historians have spoken relatively little of Vipsania. They agree, however, in reproaching her for a certain indolence.

TIBERIUS. Indolence! They call that indolence! What fools!

ANNOUNCER. Well, if you got along together, that's all that matters. . . .

TIBERIUS. Yes, but there was Julia.

ANNOUNCER. Julia? Which Julia?

TIBERIUS. I scarcely need remind you that in Roman history, families are often rather complex, rather . . . involved. Particularly the great families. Someone's always being repudiated or remarried—strictly *entre nous,* of course. A real game of musical chairs, or rather musical beds. Even a cat would lose her kittens in a labyrinth like that. So listen carefully: this Julia was a daughter of Augustus' first wife, and I've already told you that his second wife was my mother. Which makes Julia practically my step-sister. Now it so happens that this step-sister of mine decided to marry Agrippa, my wife's father. So that Julia was my mother's step-daughter and at the same time her daughter-in-law's step-mother. Do you follow me?

ANNOUNCER. I—I think so.

TIBERIUS. All right, Aetius, go on. You're with Vipsania now, and you're talking to her about Julia.

AETIUS, *as Tiberius.* I ran into Julia today.

TIBERIUS. Put more feeling into it: just talking about this woman is enough to depress you.

AETIUS. I ran into Julia today, near the Forum. She wanted me to get into her litter with her. Of course I refused.

LIVIA, *as Vipsania.* Why? You might make her angry.

AETIUS. I can't help it; I get gooseflesh whenever I'm near her. I hate that kind of woman. Always busy and you never know why. Always sitting a little too close to you, always touching you, brushing her hair in your face—*charged,* like an electric eel.

LIVIA. [*reasonably*]. Julia is a little exuberant, of course.

AETIUS. I'm tired of exuberance. Who needs to be exuberant? Are you exuberant?

LIVIA. Julia is a woman of the world.

AETIUS. Vipsania, look at me. Are you being kind, or just naive? Do you think you have to defend Julia because she's your stepmother, or protect her because she's the emperor's daughter? Defend her all you like in front of your friends— but not with me. All Rome knows Julia can't even look at a man without making him her lover.

LIVIA. All Rome! You're exaggerating.

AETIUS. Not much.

LIVIA. She's always very nice to my father, very caressing.

AETIUS. I should say she is; she's caressing with everybody. Why should she make an exception of her husband?

LIVIA. You should hear her when she talks—"my love," "my darling". . .

AETIUS. Force of habit.

LIVIA. Did she make advances to you?

AETIUS. My poor Vipsania! With Julia you can't even call it making advances—it's a way of life, a kind of second nature . . . and I don't think she has a first. You know, she's probably as surprised as anyone else by some of the men she finds herself with. . . . Ah, how comfortable it is here: these cushions, this calm, this silence. I wonder why men hate silence so? Who are they afraid of meeting—themselves?

LIVIA. Be careful—there she is.

AETIUS. [*distractedly*]. Who?

LIVIA. Julia.

AETIUS. [*horrified*]. Julia!

TIBERIUS. Julia herself. Who else would get herself up like that? Who else would be wearing those feathers, those jewels, that color hair?

JULIA. Ah, my ideal couple! Tiberius! Vipsania! Here you are at the peak of the afternoon, stretched out on cushions, the very image of activity. [*pointedly*] Vipsania, dear, I have something to say to your husband.

AETIUS. But——

JULIA. Affairs of state, my dear. Leave us.

TIBERIUS. You see what I mean. Someone in her way, immediately she invokes the state. . . .

JULIA. Well, now, Tiberius, why do I have to chase you all the way home to say two words to you? Why did you refuse to get into my litter?

AETIUS. They were expecting me at the Senate.

JULIA. I would have taken you to the Senate.

AETIUS. I rather like walking, you know.

JULIA. Don't walk too much.

AETIUS. What do you mean?

JULIA. There, it worked again. Men are marvelous! All you have to do is say anything to them—anything that comes into your head, provided you say it sententiously, with a dour look, and right away they start frowning, as if there were a world of sinister meaning in your words. That's how you make a reputation as an intelligent woman. . . . Dear old Tiberius, you know, in spite of your stubbornness, you . . . interest me. Who can say why!

AETIUS. You're . . . too kind.

JULIA. You have that sulky look I like so much in my men.

AETIUS. Ouh!

JULIA. What's the matter? I just patted your cheek.

AETIUS [*embarrassed*]. It's nothing! One of your rings scratched me.

JULIA. [*mockingly*]. Scratched you! Poor Tiberius, ready to shed his blood for me?

AETIUS. I thought you wanted to talk to me about affairs of state.

JULIA. I'm the Emperor's daughter. Everything that concerns me is an affair of state.

AETIUS. Ah, in that sense. . . .

JULIA. I'll expect you at my house tomorrow.

AETIUS. Who? Me?

JULIA. Is there anyone else in the room?

AETIUS [*fumbling*]. Oh, of course. . . . My pleasure. . . .
Unless, of course, I have to go to the Senate.

JULIA. Again that Senate! It's getting to be an obsession. The
Senate can wait. Till tomorrow then. Oh, yes, my love to
Vipsania.

TIBERIUS [*An outburst*] And that's just what she was like.
Shameless, brazen, ignoring everything except what she
wanted. . . . Aetius, let's have the scene with the deaf man
now. . . .

AETIUS [*in his own voice*]. The deaf man, my lord?

CORNELIUS [*hastily*]. Yes, the deaf man. The scene we re-
hearsed last week.

AETIUS. Oh yes, of course. [*As Tiberius*] Hola! Someone! Ah,
Cassius! Go get me that gardener, the one who takes care
of the pelargoniums. The one who's deaf.

CASSIUS. At once, my lord.

TIBERIUS. Because I had to talk about it to someone. A problem you can't talk about is like a bottle of ink overturned.
It dirties everything, and you find spots on the oddest places.
Usually I could open my heart to Vipsania, but this time I
couldn't. You'll agree with me it was a delicate matter. And
who else could I speak to about it? To my friend—did I have
any friends? They would have gone to the Emperor at once.
It would have caused talk, it would have caused trouble. . . .

AETIUS, *as Tiberius*. Ah, here's our man now! I suppose you
are really deaf?

DEAF MAN. Yes, my lord.

AETIUS [*worried*]. Cassius. . . .

CASSIUS. No, my lord. Rest assured: he answers yes no matter
what is said to him, but he is truly deaf.

AETIUS [*suspicious*]. We'll see about that. In a city like Rome where even the walls have ears, why shouldn't the deaf hear? [*slyly*] My good man, I'm going to have you hanged.

DEAF MAN. Yes, my lord.

AETIUS. He's deaf all right. Cassius, leave us. Now you listen to me—at least look as if you were listening. That's all I ask. You can't imagine how lucky you are not to be able to hear: how much you are spared. I always shudder whenever I see a man start talking. Out of this opening in the middle of our faces, out of this cavern marches a procession of everything that spoils life—worries, duties, questions, promises. The soul is a pond, smooth as a pond—why throw stones into it? Why throw words? Listen, do you know what's happening to me?

DEAF MAN. Yes, my lord.

AETIUS. Julia likes me. Julia wants me, but I don't want her. I DON'T WANT HER. I'm within my rights, aren't I?

DEAF MAN. Yes, my lord.

AETIUS. First of all, the woman wears me out. Just seeing her gives me a headache. She makes me nervous.

DEAF MAN. Yes, my lord.

AETIUS. It's wonderful! When I speak to other men, the ones who can hear, they always answer me with nonsense. This man always says the same thing and one time out of two his answer is right. That's enough to give you a good idea how much human intelligence is worth. You tell me—no, don't tell me anything. Julia is the Emperor's daughter. One doesn't refuse the Emperor's daughter. And even with the others it isn't so easy. But at least the others usually go about it with allusions. And you can always pretend not to understand allusions. With Julia everything's so clear: "I'll expect you at my house tomorrow." It's obvious she has her own ideas about the value of allusions. How can I get out of it? It's all so unfair! If a woman refuses, we say she's virtuous; but if a man does, then everybody laughs. Why? What makes the difference?

DEAF MAN. Yes, my lord.

AETIUS. And then, women, after all. You—what do you think of women, deaf man? Not just one, not two or three, but all of them, the whole tribe. . . .

DEAF MAN. Yes, my lord.

TIBERIUS. All right, that's enough of the deaf man. At the last minute, I didn't have to go to Julia's anyway. The next time we saw each other, she didn't even refer to it. I thought she had forgotten. Fickle as she was. . . . But there we were, with Agrippa dying. I'll spare you the details of the funeral ceremony. Besides, Julia behaved very well, I have to admit that. Very dignified, very slow, her face drawn. She must have decided mourning was becoming to her. Then one day Ovidius Naso, the Emperor's confidant, arrived at my house.

OVIDIUS NASO. I've come to see you on behalf of the Emperor.

AETIUS. You are welcome.

OVIDIUS NASO. Since the death of your father-in-law, the late lamented Agrippa, the Emperor has been troubled.

AETIUS [solemnly]. Of course, Agrippa's death has been a great loss for Rome.

OVIDIUS NASO [not very convinced]. Yes, a great loss for Rome, and for his wife as well. Julia is a widow; that is what particularly troubles the Emperor.

AETIUS. Believe me, it troubles me too.

OVIDIUS NASO. This solitude. . . . For her, especially.

AETIUS. My feelings, precisely.

OVIDIUS NASO. The Emperor desires Julia to remarry.

AETIUS [enthusiastically]. The Emperor is wise. The Emperor is kind. I applaud his wisdom. Certainly, Julia must remarry.

OVIDIUS NASO. She herself, moreover, is entirely in accord with her father's views.

AETIUS. Ah, that doesn't surprise me. Julia is reason itself.

OVIDIUS NASO. She wishes to remarry quite soon. And she has even made her choice—already.

AETIUS [*roguishly*]. Ahha! And who is the miserable victim?

OVIDIUS NASO [*censoriously*]. Tiberius, we are speaking of the daughter of the Emperor!

AETIUS. Of course. I meant, who is the lucky man?

OVIDIUS NASO. Your remarks scarcely encourage me to continue.

AETIUS. Please do. I assure you that in the family Julia's marriage will occasion us all infinite relief.

OVIDIUS NASO. You know Julia, once she's made up her mind about something. . . .

AETIUS. Good for her! In such matters, one must never hesitate.

OVIDIUS NASO. Her choice will perhaps not be to everyone's taste.

AETIUS. What does it matter! After all, the Emperor's daughter. . . .

OVIDIUS NASO. The lucky man, to borrow your expression, is not yet *au courant*.

AETIUS. No! He's not? How funny! Who is it?

OVIDIUS NASO. Suppose he wasn't willing. . . .

AETIUS. Wasn't willing to marry the Emperor's daughter? Then he'd be made to. But who is he?

OVIDIUS NASO. You.

AETIUS. Me?

OVIDIUS NASO. You.

AETIUS. [*exasperated*]. No. Oh no! Can't I ever get out of this? What have I ever done to Julia?

OVIDIUS NASO. You please her. . . .

AETIUS. But she doesn't happen to please me.

OVIDIUS NASO. Tiberius, the Emperor's daughter. . . .

AETIUS. So?

OVIDIUS NASO. Just a moment ago, you yourself were saying. . . .

AETIUS. No, I was talking about someone else.

OVIDIUS NASO. Does that make any difference?

AETIUS. First of all, I'm already married.

OVIDIUS NASO. This detail has not escaped the Emperor's discernment. He authorizes you to repudiate Vipsania.

AETIUS. Authorizes me? But I don't want to.

OVIDIUS NASO. In this matter, someone has wanted to in your place.

AETIUS. It's easy for you to talk. Would you accept?

OVIDIUS NASO. With my eyes closed.

AETIUS. Do you like Julia?

OVIDIUS NASO. I said: with my eyes closed.

AETIUS. But really, it's indecent! I can't marry my mother-in-law.

OVIDIUS NASO. She is your mother-in-law no longer: her husband is dead; and she was only his second wife.

AETIUS. We're still related. . . .

OVIDIUS. Not according to law. Moreover, by repudiating Vipsania, you completely annul this already vague relationship.

AETIUS. And what about her lovers? Have you thought about that? You know as well as I do about Julia's annoying habit of taking lovers.

OVIDIUS NASO. Tsk! Tsk! A husband should not speak of his wife in such a way.

AETIUS. She isn't my wife yet.

OVIDIUS NASO. She will be. And you will be the son-in-law of the Emperor. The latter has no sons. . . .

AETIUS. That hardly seems a reason to tolerate the fact that my wife takes lovers. And what lovers! Gladiators, stable boys. . . .

OVIDIUS NASO. You are not obliged to associate with them. The Emperor's daughter, Tiberius . . . the Emperor will not revoke his decision. . . . Nor will Julia.

TIBERIUS. Well, after all, I had to give in. Oh, I tried to struggle, of course, but there was really nothing I could do. I had to repudiate Vipsania and marry Julia. It didn't take long. A few months later, I called in Ovidius Naso to help me.

OVIDIUS NASO. I came at once.

AETIUS, *as Tiberius*. No, no, no! I will not endure her a moment longer. She is impossible.

OVIDIUS NASO. Who?

AETIUS. Who do you think? Julia—always Julia! Who else? Sometimes it seems to me there's no one else on earth: she's infested everything. She's always looming over the horizon. And she's my wife!

OVIDIUS NASO. Tiberius, she's the——

AETIUS. She's the Emperor's daughter, I know. Unfortunately, she's also my wife. I don't know what's got into her. She's in a frenzy: it's not one lover a week; it's a lover a day.

OVIDIUS NASO. The Emperor has been informed, and deplores the fact as much as you.

AETIUS. That's it; we'll cry over it together. If only she could arrange matters so no one would know anything about it. All I ask is a little peace and quiet. But even in her orgies, she's still the same rude, noisy, arrogant, intolerable Julia. Last night a patrol found her in the middle of the Forum with a crowd of drunkards—she was in the arms of lousy——

OVIDIUS NASO. I know. . . .

AETIUS. Ah, you know, but I'm her husband. I make scenes. It's as if I were singing songs. Have you ever made Julia a scene? If you haven't you're missing something. I don't even have time to open my mouth before she starts talking; I say three words, she says fifteen. I shout, she shouts louder. Once it's over, I'm always the one who's in the wrong. Before three minutes have passed, I'm running around and around in her tirades like a bug in a box.

OVIDIUS NASO. What do you want to do?

AETIUS. I want to go away. [*Forcefully*] I want to go away.

I've already served as a governor in the provinces; it doesn't matter where to this time—just so as it's as far away as possible.

OVIDIUS NASO. They'll say it's exile.

AETIUS. My real exile has been Julia. Look at me: I've lost weight, I don't sleep any more. Tell the Emperor about that. He knows his daughter; he'll understand.

OVIDIUS NASO. I'm afraid he will not understand.

AETIUS. Then let me take a trip, a long trip.

OVIDIUS NASO. You are the Emperor's successor. I doubt that he will consider such a trip very opportune.

AETIUS. Be careful, Ovidius Naso. Don't go too far. If I have to, I'll go shout it in the Forum; I'll speak to the Senate; I'll go on a hunger strike.

TIBERIUS. And that's what I did—I went on a hunger strike. It didn't take long, either. The Emperor capitulated quite soon. Fortunately. Have you ever gone on a hunger strike? It's terrible. I don't know what it comes from, but suddenly you have one of those cravings! Especially since I like to eat. The pleasures of the table are one thing I am rather fond of. Well, finally they let me go. And ever since, historians have asked themselves: why did Tiberius run away to the island of Rhodes? Was it a political maneuver, or a fit of misanthropy? Historians exist to put little things into big works. Every gossip in Rome knew the answer: Tiberius was running away from his wife. Retreat before his wife's lovers. What else could he do, considering their number. . . . Tiberius was escaping from scenes, from screams. The problem with a wife who has lovers—is not so much that she's unfaithful. You get used to that. The problem is that everything gets upset: it's the disorder, the racket, the unswept floors, the slamming doors, the ground giving way under your feet—nothing is stable any more. On the island of Rhodes, I found calm and silence again. At last. Which is probably why I've never been fond of the Atlantic; the waves, the undertow—it all makes too much noise. Now the Mediterranean. . . . Why look, nine days out of ten it's like a great pool of silence. You know the island of Rhodes?

ANNOUNCER. Why no, I've never been there.

TIBERIUS. It's something like Capri. . . . I took walks; I rested. You'll understand how much Julia had wrecked my life if I tell you this: I had to make *an effort* to rest, had to impose a discipline on myself, struggle against my nerves. Yes, yes, I really did. At first I would get up at dawn—anxious, worried, as if I still had things to do. Restless women are like that; they're contagious. They spoil other people's relaxation too. I had to learn all over again how to let myself drift with the days as they passed. And to do that, I had to empty those days first. Had to make them into—not days, but stretches of time where there would be nothing but trifles, matters of no importance. Now and then I would summon a few grammarians to discuss commas. Grammatical discussions never break the silence: they make it stand out all the clearer, like punctuation.

ANNOUNCER. Speaking of grammarians, I've read somewhere that you once arrested——

TIBERIUS. I said I liked discussions; I don't like to be bothered.

ANNOUNCER. And you stayed on Rhodes for a long time?

TIBERIUS. Seven years.

ANNOUNCER. Seven years?

TIBERIUS. Does that surprise you?

ANNOUNCER. Seven years, on an island. . . . There can't be much to do. . . .

TIBERIUS. It's doing things that makes time exist. Distractions, duties, diversions, they're all so many life buoys men have invented to keep from sinking. So they can always find themselves facing something, never facing themselves. Try doing

nothing for a while; nothing at all. The days will soon stop
being days.

ANNOUNCER. The time must seem long.

TIBERIUS. Who ever told you it was short? Yes, the days at
Rhodes were long. And finally I had the leisure to meet
myself again.

ANNOUNCER. Then why didn't you stay?

TIBERIUS. I was a successor. Even when they do nothing, suc-
cessors are wasting their time trying to waste time: time
works *for* them. One day the Emperor recalled me; he had
grown old; his health was declining. I found him in his little
bedroom—a real cell, with thick walls, as cool as a grotto.
We spent a whole day, facing each other, alone. . . .

ANNOUNCER [*anxious*]. What did he tell you?

TIBERIUS [*vague*]. Oh, things. [*Pulling himself together*]
Young man, I'm going to tell you. I've tried to have my
slaves act out that scene too. It seemed interesting to me.
Just from the historical point of view. That kind of . . .
transmission of power, that relay, that torch handed from
one man to another. And you know, I couldn't do it. For me,
there isn't much I can call sacred. Except perhaps this—the
memory of that old man who talked to me. No, not of that
old man. There in front of him, to keep from panicking, I
kept telling myself: it's nothing, it's only an old man, an old
man like all the rest, an old man who's going to die. This is
not true! An emperor, especially if he's reigned for a long
time, is no longer a man like all the rest. And a man that's
going to die—he's not like all the rest either. The majesty of
the Emperor, the majesty of death—no, that's not quite what
I mean. It was more like secrets. Two terrible secrets . . .
death, power. . . . In that tiny room, facing that dying
Emperor, it seemed to me as if I were being initiated into
secrets. . . .

ANNOUNCER. But if you felt that an office was enough to give the officeholder a certain dignity, why didn't you experience it too; after all, you were an emperor too. . . .

TIBERIUS. There are certain offices that are given to the wrong people. I should have acted, but I don't like to act. That is my secret. It bored me. As I've told you. After all, what have I ever done in my life? Did I marry Julia? No, she married me. Did I succeed the Emperor? No, he named me his heir. Once you let others make decisions for you, there's nothing else to do but accept the consequences of their decisions. There's nothing else to do, young man, but become that nothingness you have never ceased being. The Emperor knew it. How that touched me, during our last interview—that desperate effort he was making to transform me, to re-create me in a few hours. He was still trying to make something out of this miserable putty. . . . He told me.

AUGUSTUS. You're slow, Tiberius. I pity Rome, falling between jaws so slow. Yet our failings—are perhaps failings only when they're bashful. Make your failing into a doctrine—indulge it to extremes, rigorously, and it will serve you as well as any virtue. You're slow, Tiberius: be slower still.

TIBERIUS. And I have been slow. During my reign, everything slowed down. And it was no worse that way.

CORNELIUS. From the very first, you were slow to make up your mind. For weeks on end, you left the Empire in ignorance as to whether you would accept the succession from Augustus.

TIBERIUS. Delicious weeks! I waited; the whole Empire waited.

CORNELIUS. This love of indecision seems to me to be one of the essential traits in your character. And I have taken the liberty of adding a brief digression on this subject. I remember that journey you were to make into Further Gaul. You had your departure proclaimed everywhere. You had the ritual prayers offered. The chariots were already on the road with the baggage. But when the moment came—you never left.

TIBERIUS. There is a certain pitch of wisdom where you realize that in all things there are as many reasons *for* as there are reasons *against*.

ANNOUNCER. Under these conditions, why hesitate?

TIBERIUS. Under these conditions, why act?

ANNOUNCER. Choosing frees you from indecision.

TIBERIUS. Why be free? Indecision has its charm.

ANNOUNCER. Such a philosophy couldn't have made life any easier for you.

TIBERIUS. So many things fall into place of their own accord. You find yourself confronted with a problem: sleep on it. The next day, there's one chance out of two that the problem will have disappeared. So much to the good.

ANNOUNCER. A curious doctrine for an emperor.

TIBERIUS. Every medal has its reverse, from which it follows that every reverse has its medal. Since I made decisions only rarely, it was not often that they turned out badly. Since I believed in nothing, I was tolerant. During my reign, speech and thought were free.

CORNELIUS. In you, perhaps, this was a form of contempt.

TIBERIUS. Don't look for motives; be satisfied with results. On the other hand, I was very strict about morals. I don't know why. But a certain license in behavior always bothered me.

ANNOUNCER. That's peculiar. Is moral order a characteristic preoccupation of idleness?

TIBERIUS. Well, take adultery, you might think that, given my nature, it would have no effect on me. Well, you'd be quite wrong. To me it seems perfectly monstrous that a woman already furnished with one man should go and encumber herself with another.

ANNOUNCER. Then in the long run, if I take your meaning correctly, what you object to in adulterous women is that they're more active than the others, in a way . . . ?

TIBERIUS. In a way, yes. Marriage is peace. Otherwise what good is it? I enacted a law forcing deceived husbands to sue for divorce. And I had to force them, my friend. Could you believe it? One man I knew, for instance, a senator—well, his wife was unfaithful to him with his son-in-law, and believe it or not, he didn't want to divorce her.

ANNOUNCER. He was merely applying your doctrine.

TIBERIUS. There was no need for *him* to apply it. A doctrine is strictly personal.

ANNOUNCER. That is doubtless the principle which permitted you to reform the morals of the period without reforming your own.

TIBERIUS. What do you mean?

ANNOUNCER. I hope you will excuse me if I broach a subject . . . but after all, you belong to history. Nothing about you is a matter of indifference to history. And as for morals, you have a . . . a reputation.

TIBERIUS. Oh, my reputation. . . .

ANNOUNCER. There has been talk of orgies, debauches. It has been said that you retired here, to Capri, only to abandon yourself to your dreadful instincts.

TIBERIUS. Gossip! Whenever anyone talks about an emperor, there always seems to be a need to embroider. Livia!

LIVIA. Yes, my lord.

TIBERIUS. You're here every day: do you think we do such terrible things here? Tell the gentleman.

LIVIA. Terrible things, my lord? Oh no! I would have noticed. A little party now and then.

TIBERIUS. You see, a little party. . . .

ANNOUNCER. There's never smoke without fire.

TIBERIUS. That's always the excuse of slanderers. But you know as well as I do that sometimes there's a great deal of smoke for a very little fire. Just because someone heard laughter behind a curtain, right away people start imagining things. Perhaps it was only a game of blindman's buff.

ANNOUNCER. Suetonius is categorical. He gives details!

TIBERIUS. I indulged myself in a few amusements. To a historian, of course, an emperor's amusements always seem monstrous.

ANNOUNCER. There have been rumors about slaves thrown into the sea. . . .

TIBERIUS. Absurd! Look for yourself. With all those rocks down there, the slaves would have been dead long before they reached the water.

ANNOUNCER. They would have been dead all the same.

TIBERIUS. Do you think this business of the slaves sounds much like me?

ANNOUNCER. No, not altogether. But boredom can make anyone ferocious.

TIBERIUS. How do you know? Have you ever been bored?

ANNOUNCER. Of course!

TIBERIUS. And you felt like throwing your slaves into the sea?

ANNOUNCER. I should say not!

TIBERIUS. Then you don't know what you're talking about.

ANNOUNCER. All right, I'll concede that point. Anyway, we've come as far as your stay in Capri. Why did you come here?

TIBERIUS. Why did thousands of tourists come here every year? The island is beautiful.

ANNOUNCER. That's not what I mean. Why did you leave Rome?

TIBERIUS. I don't like Rome; there's too much noise.

ANNOUNCER. I'm asking you for a serious explanation; thousands of people may be listening to us. Noisy or not, Rome was the capital of your Empire; you were the Emperor. . . .

TIBERIUS. Power no longer interested me.

ANNOUNCER. You could have abdicated.

TIBERIUS. What difference would that have made? Two emperors instead of one? I prefer leaving things in suspense.

ANNOUNCER. In suspense, a whole empire in suspense?

TIBERIUS. An empire goes by itself—of its own accord, at least for a while. I took that while for myself, that's all.

ANNOUNCER. You were deserting your post.

TIBERIUS. I stepped back, which is not at all the same thing; I was keeping my distance. Then, you know, a government may have certain advantages, but it also has *dis*advantages. Don't you think the two cancel each other out?

ANNOUNCER. The theory can be argued.

TIBERIUS. For seventy-five per cent of the cases, bureaucracy is enough. That's why it exists: to give things their true rhythm. As for current affairs, which fortunately are not current at all but as stagnant as you please, I can assure you that during my reign, the Romans, left somewhat to themselves, were not unhappy.

ANNOUNCER. Yet there has been mention of certain excesses.

TIBERIUS. Give me an example.

ANNOUNCER. Wait a minute, let me try to remember. Oh, yes, there was the daughter of your minister Sejanus. You are said to have had her executed.

TIBERIUS. Sejanus was a rascal; he betrayed me in every possible way. The people were happy to hear of his death.

ANNOUNCER. I'm speaking of the daughter, not the father. . . . Besides wasn't there a law, a law which quite precisely forbade the execution of virgins?

TIBERIUS. And you think it's fair to exempt virgins like that?

ANNOUNCER. I'm not saying it was fair; I'm saying there was a law. This virgin could not be executed.

TIBERIUS. Which is why I made sure she was violated by a guard on the day before her execution.

ANNOUNCER. How terrible!

TIBERIUS. I beg your pardon?

ANNOUNCER. I'm sorry! With twenty centuries between us. . . . I meant that if you interpret it that way, respect for the law is nothing more than derision.

TIBERIUS. My dear young man, you must tell me what it is you want. If I had had her executed while she was still a virgin,

you would have reproached me for not having respected the
law. I have respected the law and you're still not satisfied.

ANNOUNCER. You shouldn't have executed her at all.

TIBERIUS [*indifferent*]. That. . . .

ANNOUNCER. Besides, there were other deaths, other cruelties.

TIBERIUS. Yes, go on. . . .

ANNOUNCER. Your wife Julia—whom you starved to
death. . . .

TIBERIUS. Don't talk to me about Julia. You've seen how she
treated me. No, I hadn't forgiven her. And do you think she
had forgiven me? Did she have any pity for me? What right
did she have to overturn my life, to disturb my happiness?
Besides, I didn't kill her. I merely reduced her expenditures.

ANNOUNCER. You must have reduced them considerably to
make her die of hunger.

TIBERIUS. Bah! Julia never knew how to organize. . . .

ANNOUNCER. And the second husband of your wife Vipsania?

TIBERIUS. A crime of passion.

ANNOUNCER. What do you mean, a crime of passion? You had
him executed!

TIBERIUS. A crime of passion committed—indirectly. Other
men use daggers; I used the law. An emperor's weapon!
Could I permit another man to be my wife's husband?

ANNOUNCER. But you had repudiated her!

TIBERIUS. That was no reason. I still loved her; he should have
understood that. No, no, don't insist. We are talking about
the labyrinth of the heart. And after all, with all your historians, you've only cited three victims, including one husband, which doesn't count. As a favor to you, I'm perfectly
willing to include those few slaves whom I had completely
forgotten about. Multiply the total by ten, multiply it by a
hundred—it still makes fewer victims than any of my predecessors had in one of their stupid little wars.

ANNOUNCER. I'm sorry, but it's hardly the same thing.

TIBERIUS. I don't see the difference! Well, yes, there is one of course; the soldiers are innocent. Could you say as much for Julia? . . . You know Roman history?

ANNOUNCER. A little, yes.

TIBERIUS. Have you never been struck by how many of us died young?

ANNOUNCER. Yes. A matter of public health, I suppose. Or the relatively backward state of medicine.

TIBERIUS. Medicine, if you like. But my dear young man, have you ever really thought about it? Among people whose mortality rate is high, human life has infinitely less value. For us, a dead man is not a matter of importance. That is one thing you shouldn't lose sight of in writing our biographies.

ANNOUNCER. There's one more death . . . for which you are not directly responsible, I hasten to admit.

TIBERIUS. The death of Jesus?

ANNOUNCER. Yes.

TIBERIUS. That was certainly my last piece of bad luck. I had removed myself from Rome, absented myself from power, made every effort to make my reign into something that would leave scarcely any trace behind. But when fate wills, it comes to seek us out even on islands. Here I was, daydreaming. And at the same time, out there in Palestine, my reign was assuming this enormous burden. The death of Jesus . . . which was going to change so many things. Which was going to make the world turn beneath my feet. . . . Sometimes I wonder if this dreadful reputation that's attributed to me, this sort of . . . malediction upon me, is not simply the malediction that weighs on everyone who was involved in that death. Herod, Caiphas, Pontius Pilate. . . . You know, I knew Pontius Pilate. He was nothing but a good official, an honest man who wanted to avoid trouble more than anything else. He washed his hands of the whole affair. And now, there he is for all eternity, paralyzed in that ridiculous ablution.

All for what? For a tiny incident, the kind that happens every day. In occupied territory, you know! . . . A death without importance. . . . And now it seems that this death was not without importance. How could we have guessed? We were like people who are going to be involved in a trial and don't know it yet. Who come and go without suspecting that in a few weeks a floodlight will be turned on them and that in its harsh light all their actions will become ambiguous, suspect, culpable.

ANNOUNCER. Apropos, there's a story——

TIBERIUS. Yes, I've heard it. . . . It's strange, you know, I was here, here in this very place. It was in the afternoon, Cornelius was here with me. Do you remember, Cornelius? You said to me:

CORNELIUS. My lord, I see a galley has just put into harbor.

TIBERIUS. Right there, you see, down below. That's where the harbor was in my time. In that bay they call Tragara now.

CORNELIUS. A man is being put ashore; he must be a messenger.

TIBERIUS. I hope it's not bad news.

CORNELIUS. I don't think so. Messengers with bad news run. This man is taking his time. It must be one of your governors' weekly reports.

TIBERIUS. I even made a bet with Cornelius.

CORNELIUS. The Emperor is occasionally good enough to lay wagers with me.

TIBERIUS. Was this messenger from Spain, from Cappadocia, from Thrace or from Palestine? I put my money on Palestine.

CORNELIUS. I put mine on Spain. We watched the man from above. He climbed toward us up the path.

TIBERIUS. With his steady postman's gait. As he passed, he tore off a leaf from the lentiscus tree, rubbed it between his fingers, and sniffed the aroma.

CORNELIUS. He was here. . . .

TIBERIUS. I had won. It was the messenger from Palestine.

CORNELIUS. He handed me the report.

TIBERIUS. A day like any other. A messenger like any other. The ordinary routine of power. I can still see him—that man. Motionless, a lentiscus leaf between his fingers, a sword cut on his cheek. The sea was calm. Down below, a slave was singing. Cornelius read the report.

CORNELIUS [reading]. Political situation . . .

TIBERIUS. Skip that. The reflections of governors on the political situation are never anything but hypotheses.

CORNELIUS. The economic situation . . .

TIBERIUS. Figures. . . . I'll look into that later.

CORNELIUS. Roads and bridges . . .

TIBERIUS. Of no interest.

CORNELIUS. There's a note. [Reading] At the request of the people and the persons of influence, I have had an agitator named Jesus executed.

TIBERIUS. An agitator named Jesus. . . . I hadn't even been paying attention. And then suddenly, from one second to the next, the sky darkened. [Thunder clap.] There was lightning, thunder . . . [Lightning.] And from down there, over there—you see? Across there, toward Sorrento, I heard a voice.

[We hear a long groan, and then in the distance a loud voice shouting.]

LOUD VOICE. The Great God Pan is dead! The Great God Pan is dead!

TIBERIUS. The Great God Pan! As if a crack zigzagged across the Empire, like the lightning through the torn sky. The Great God Pan was dead. A world was dying, and with its last breath came a terrible cry.

ANNOUNCER [anguished]. But is it true? I've heard the story; but did it really happen or is it only a legend?

TIBERIUS. Legend or truth—how do I know? When Jesus was summoned before him, Pontius Pilate asked him "What is truth?" As if he had a vague presentiment that he was living through one of those moments when instead of everyday truth, which may be only an apparent truth—he would be dealing with a truth of trials, a truth of judges, a truth of history. And from having been told the story of that cry so often, perhaps I finished by imagining I heard it myself. What does it matter? With or without the cry, something had just happened, something. . . .

ANNOUNCER [*after a pause*]. And afterwards?

TIBERIUS. Afterwards? Nothing. I went on living. For a long time still, too long.

CORNELIUS. You died thirty-seven years after Jesus Christ was born. You were seventy-nine years old.

ANNOUNCER. You went on living here?

TIBERIUS. Yes, still on Capri.

ANNOUNCER. And what did you find here?

TIBERIUS. What I had already found on Rhodes. What you find on islands: detachment, selection, silence. And, in this silence, how shall I put it, the . . . the decomposition, you might say, of my boredom. My boredom, yes, I think it dissolved here under the sun, evaporated into the warm air. I suppressed time, and in this nothingness I lost that terrible sense of being only nothingness myself. You can see for yourself, there must be something in the air here. A certain magic secreted by the sea and the rocks. Twenty centuries after me, the men who come here. . . . Well, just listen to them.

[*Uproar.*]

FOURTEENTH VOICE, *a man* [*bored tone*] *Comment allez-vous?*

SIXTEENTH VOICE, *a woman*. What shall we do today?

TWENTIETH VOICE, *a man*. Have you heard? Koko's with Bobby now!

EIGHTEENTH VOICE, *a woman* [*yawning*]. I think I'll go back to the hotel and take a nap.

TIBERIUS. Twenty centuries after me—twenty centuries after my death and it's as if I had never ceased to weigh on this island. Men still come here looking for the same thing; like myself, men still come here to forget life, to kill time. To kill time: perhaps that's one way to kill your soul.

[THE END]